MW00779451

A DIFFERENT FRAME OF MIND

Living a Full Life
with Traumatic Brain Injury

Lois Jean Thomas

Seventh Child Publishing, LLC
Saint Joseph, Michigan

Names and other characteristics of the people appearing in this book have been changed to protect their anonymity.

Cover design by A.R. Thomas and Lois Jean Thomas

ISBN-13: 978-0-9976445-4-8

Library of Congress Control Number: 2018903113

Lois Jean Thomas, Saint Joseph, Michigan

For my husband and my three children,
who help me live a fuller life.

CONTENTS

ACKNOWLEDGEMENTS

As always, I offer my profound gratitude to my husband for his contributions in bringing this book to completion. He helped with editing, formatting, and cover design. He offered encouragement and moral support as I struggled my way through the manuscript. For weeks on end, he spared me visual strain by reading aloud to me what I had already written, so that I could detect where corrections needed to be made.

Russ, it would have been impossible to do this without you.

A DIFFERENT FRAME OF MIND

Living a Full Life
with Traumatic Brain Injury

INTRODUCTION

Four years ago, I published a book entitled *Days of Daze: My Journey Through the World of Traumatic Brain Injury.* In that memoir, I recount the story of how I was struck by a car while crossing the street on my lunch hour at work, sustaining a brain injury that brought my career in clinical social work to a premature end. I describe the bewildering symptoms of my brain injury, and my efforts to adjust to my new reality.

In 2016, while participating in a medical exercise program associated with a local physical therapy clinic, I befriended a woman named Gloria. As she and I became acquainted with each other, we shared our stories of recovery from physical trauma. She told me about undergoing numerous surgeries after breaking multiple bones in a fall down a flight of stairs. In turn, I told her about sustaining a traumatic brain injury.

I informed Gloria that I'd written *Days of Daze*, and she requested a copy of it. After reading it, she said to me, "Why don't you write another book telling us how you're doing now?"

I went home and talked to my husband about Gloria's suggestion. "I've recently been thinking the same thing," he told me.

And so, undertaking this project seemed like the right thing to do, to move beyond my account of the acute phase of my recovery in *Days of Days,* and to describe my efforts to cope with long-term challenges.

I'm doing somewhat better than I was at the time I began writing *Days of Days.* I've shown improvement in some of my symptoms. More importantly, I've become more adept at dealing with the lingering problems. Since I've lived with these challenges for more than seven years, I understand them better and am less bewildered by them. My coping skills are more finely honed.

I consider myself to be fortunate, as many individuals who sustain traumatic brain injuries are left with far more severe challenges than I am forced to deal with. Some people are incredulous when I tell them about my brain injury. Some who knew about the injury from the beginning seem to have forgotten that it happened. I hear comments such as, "You're doing so well," or, "You're so strong."

I don't look like I have a disability. A mild brain injury is often not readily apparent to others. To the outside world, I appear to be a reserved, soft-spoken, ordinary-looking woman. The only thing that will arouse your curiosity when you encounter me in a store, a restaurant, or any other public building is that I will be wearing sunglasses. Otherwise, my impairments are subtle, and most people aren't aware of them. I hide them well.

But my husband Russ certainly knows about my challenges, as he lives with them. He is inextricably linked with my efforts to negotiate life, and his support is crucial for me. The new reality imposed by my injury has altered his role in our marriage.

Daily life is harder for me since my injury. I face ordinary life challenges with depleted resources and stamina. Much of the time, I live in a state of low-grade cognitive and sensory frustration that occasionally escalates to agonizing proportions.

As I set about writing this book, I am forced to admit to a self-serving motivation. Because when I am communicating with others in the hopes of encouraging them, I am speaking to myself as well, sorting out what happened to me, convincing myself that I can persevere.

This book is not meant to be an authoritative resource on the topic of traumatic brain injury. It is only my story. I have no right or intention to speak for anyone else. While people who sustain brain injuries may share many similar symptoms, no two injuries are exactly alike. Each traumatic brain injury impacts a distinctive personality and disrupts a particular lifestyle. The loss of former capabilities means different things to different people, and they grieve over these losses for different reasons. And each TBI survivor develops his or her unique ways of coping with impairment.

The chapters in this book are arbitrary divisions. Truthfully, all my challenges are interrelated and intertwined. Cognitive, sensory, physical, and emotional symptoms all impact each other and are not easily separated out as discrete problems. I ask you to keep this in mind as you read my story.

THE HILL AT FOX'S CORNER

Several months after I sustained my brain injury, I received an email from my sister Rhonda. "I was thinking about your accident," she wrote, "and I realized it's the second time this has happened to you."

She was right. I'd been thinking the same thing. I'd had an accident when I was fifteen, in which I'd incurred a similar head injury.

A year or two before my accident in 2010, recollections of my childhood injury came up to haunt me in a new way. Because the memories were weighing so heavily on my mind, I set up an appointment with my energy healer, Wanda. During the session, I explored the impact of that accident more deeply than I'd ever done before. I wondered at the fact that my life had been spared, as I easily could have left this world as a teenager. Looking back, it seems that I needed to process the impact of the first accident before I was forced to cope with the one that was soon to come.

I grew up in a rural area of Brown County, Indiana, on the outskirts of Beanblossom, a tiny village with a population of no more than several hundred people. Our family of eleven was crammed into a shabby three-bedroom house with no indoor bathroom. With my father as the only breadwinner, our finances were stretched to the limit. Luxuries rarely came our way.

Being Mennonite imposed additional restrictions on our lifestyle. Females in our church were not allowed to cut their hair, or to wear jewelry, makeup, or slacks. My parents didn't allow us children to attend movies, dances, or any other activities they deemed to be worldly. We were never permitted to set foot in Beanblossom's bluegrass festivals, which were held less than a mile from our home.

We had no television to watch. We subscribed to no daily newspapers or popular magazines. I didn't have access to a radio until I was in my teens. Thus, in my early years, I was cut off from many cultural influences.

With little else to do, my siblings and I spent a great deal of time outdoors, playing in the yard and the nearby creek, or roaming the wooded hills behind our home.

As I entered my teen years, our restricted lifestyle left me feeling bored and restless. Self-conscious teenagers that we were, my sisters and I hated the fact that we looked like oddities among our peers. We put on jewelry and applied makeup behind our parents' backs, and fought with them for the right to wear slacks. Grudgingly, my mom and dad finally allowed us to each own a single pair of jeans, which were meant to be worn only for activities in which a skirt failed to provide sufficient modesty.

When I was a freshman in high school, my sisters and I inherited two castoff bicycles from my older brothers. This seemed like a rare luxury, even though the bikes were too big for us to ride comfortably. I often entertained myself by donning my jeans and jumping on one of those old bikes, taking off for an adventure on Gatesville Road, the country road on which my family lived.

The rural roads in our county were narrow, winding, and hilly, marked by blind curves and one-lane bridges. Riding in my father's car as a young child, I'd become accustomed to what happened when two vehicles approached a one-lane bridge from opposite directions. One vehicle needed to stop to allow the other vehicle passage through the bridge. Because of my father's kind and conscientious nature, he was, no doubt, the driver who tended to grant the other vehicle the right to pass first.

One spring day when I was nearing the end of my freshman year, I found the interminably long Sunday afternoon hours to be unbearably boring. So, I decided to take a ride on one of the hand-me-down bikes. I headed east on Gatesville Road, away from Beanblossom toward an even more remote rural area of the county.

I had a particular destination in mind: Fox's Corner. This landmark consisted of a single commercial enterprise, a gas station and small store located at the intersection of Gatesville Road and Beanblossom Road. I knew that if I turned left at Fox's Corner onto Beanblossom Road, it would take me down a very steep hill. And riding down that hill at top speed was going to be my thrill for the day.

Everything went as I'd planned. After riding several miles, I reached Fox's Corner and made my left turn. As I approached my descent down the steep hill, I pedaled furiously, picking up speed to maximize my thrill.

At the bottom of the hill was a one-lane bridge. As I flew down the hill, I saw a car approaching the bridge from the opposite direction. Additionally, two children were crossing the bridge on foot. I quickly calculated that there was no room on that bridge for a bicycle rider, and that if I continued my course, a collision with either the car or the children was inevitable.

So, while traveling at top speed, I slammed on the handbrakes of a bicycle I was not fully accustomed to riding.

I woke up lying on my back in a shallow ditch alongside the road. A few people were milling around and standing over me. I tried to make sense of where I was and why I was there. When I was finally able to speak, I asked a strange question: "Is this Sunday?" I remembered that I'd gone out on a bike ride on a Sunday afternoon, and wondered whether it was still the same day.

Within minutes, an ambulance arrived, bringing my mother to the scene. I later learned that someone had gone to our house, informing my parents that one of their children had been in an accident.

Everything after that happened matter-of-factly. My mother did not appear to be alarmed about the accident. I suspect that, for her, it was all part of the wear and tear associated with raising a large brood of children. The ambulance transported me to a doctor's office in the nearby small town of Nashville, as the closest hospital was thirty miles away. The local doctor on call came to the clinic to check me over.

I had a very painful contusion on the right side of my head. I learned that when I'd slammed on the brakes, I'd flown off the bike and landed on my head. The doctor said I'd sustained a mild concussion. I also had other contusions on the right side of my body.

The clothing I was wearing was torn when my body skidded across the pavement. That saddened me, as I'd ruined my favorite shirt and the only pair of jeans I owned. The bicycle I was riding sustained no damage.

As I was weak and dazed from my head injury, I was kept

out of school for a week. I recall my mother helping me wash my long hair, as the bump on my head was very sore.

But my main cause of distress was how I looked. My right eye was swollen shut, the area around it grotesquely discolored in shades of black, yellow, and purple. When I returned to school, I still looked ghastly. I remember one insensitive boy doubling over with laughter when he saw my face.

After my black eye cleared up, a telltale sign of my accident remained in the form of a bloody-looking spot in my right eye. This, of course, made me profoundly self-conscious about my appearance. I did my best to enhance my looks by dressing well and taking special care with my hair, but I could do nothing about that ugly spot in my eye. It remained there for many months, and I worried that it would never go away.

Thankfully, I resumed my schooling with no difficulties. I suffered no cognitive impairment from the concussion. I exhibited no behavioral changes. I passed through my teen years into adulthood with no apparent effects from that head injury, except for a deathly fear of the hill at Fox's Corner and all loss of desire to do anything daring on a bicycle.

But looking back, I recall an incident when I was sitting in the bleachers at a high school basketball game. The crowd was cheering for our team, screaming loudly. I remember how distressing that level of noise was for me, and how after that, I had little interest in attending ballgames. I question now whether my head injury had impacted my ability to handle sensory bombardment.

As an adult, I felt uncomfortable in the midst of loud noise and commotion, and tended to shy away from such situations. There is no way to link this phenomenon with my first head injury. I just wonder about it.

When I was still a young adult, I was informed by an optometrist that I had a cataract in my right eye. He said it was not the type of cataract associated with aging. Over the next several decades, every optometrist who examined my eyes mentioned the cataract. One of them told me that type of cataract was associated with head injuries. When I informed him about the concussion from my bicycle accident, he responded with, "That's probably what caused it."

Of course, there's no proof that the cataract was linked to the accident. However, I will always wonder whether that first trauma to my brain made me more vulnerable to what happened when I sustained my second injury.

Seven years after my bicycle accident, when I was a young mother living several hundred miles away from my home community, I went back to Beanblossom to visit my sister Rhonda. I also went to see my childhood friend Roseanne, who lived near Fox's Corner.

While Roseanne and I were visiting, her mother-in-law, Mrs. Ford, stopped by the house. When she saw me, she immediately identified me as the survivor of that bicycle accident. I hadn't known that my mishap had taken place in front of her house, and that she'd been an eyewitness.

Mrs. Ford launched into an account of her memory of the accident, which was still vivid in her mind. She recalled seeing me being thrown off the bicycle, flying through the air, and landing on the road.

"I thought you were a goner," she told me.

I shuddered as I realized how serious that accident had been, how narrowly I had escaped debilitating injury or death.

ON A DIFFERENT PLANE

I have a young friend named Aaron, whom I've known for about twenty years. While our contact has been sporadic, I've always felt an uncanny connection with him. Aaron is intellectually brilliant, and I thoroughly enjoy listening to his thoughts on various subjects. However, I also recognize that he has not lived a typical adult life, in that he's had challenges with such things as employment and independent living.

In the summer of 2016, I had the opportunity to connect with Aaron on a deeper level. Our conversations took place primarily through email. He'd learned that I had sustained a traumatic brain injury, and expressed his concerns. I found his sensitivity to the challenges I faced to be greater than that of almost anyone else I knew. He understood that the mechanisms through which I interacted with life had been altered. Once, he said to me, "It's like you're living on a different plane."

Aaron talked with me about his childhood developmental difficulties. He'd spent his early school years in special education, before testing revealed that he was intellectually gifted. He told me he'd recently undergone testing that determined him to be functioning on the high end of the autism spectrum.

This revelation helped me make sense of the difficulties I've known him to face in his adult life. He is now officially categorized as "disabled." However, in my mind, such as label does not apply to Aaron. A term currently in usage, "differently abled," aptly describes him, as he has abilities of intellect and insight that most of us do not possess.

Aaron told me about his younger brother David, who had been born with such profound mental and physical impairments that he needed around-the-clock care. Aaron had spent much of his adult life providing that care while his parents worked outside the home. David had died six months before Aaron and I began our communication that summer.

Knowing that I am a writer, Aaron confided that he wanted to write a book about his relationship with his brother. I encouraged him to do so, as he had some great ideas for such a project. We decided to get together to further discuss his plans.

Our designated meeting place was a popular coffee shop in Aaron's hometown. Unfortunately, we found the place to be packed with customers, and the noise level proved to be so overwhelming that I was unable to focus on our conversation. Aaron quickly understood my plight, and suggested that we move to an outdoor table where we could talk with fewer sensory distractions.

We sat under an umbrella to shield us from the stimulation of the glaring sunlight, two differently abled friends facing each other across the picnic table. I was keenly aware of the fact that neither of us quite met the criteria for normal adult functioning. Both of us had brain challenges that kept us outside what are considered to be normal parameters. Aaron was born with his challenges, while mine came through accidental trauma. Yet, a wavelength of understanding ran between us, so strong that it was almost palpable. It had to do with something that transcended troubled brains, a deep connection of unbroken spirits. I will never forget that moment.

We talked about his experience of living with autism. I told him I believed his unusual perspectives on life were valid, and that they offered something to our collective "bigger picture."

"It's like looking at life through a different lens," he told me. "Sometimes, I have a perspective that no one around me shares, and it looks like I'm wrong. But in the end, it turns out that I was right."

Aaron was still shaken by his brother's death, and was feeling adrift in the aftermath of losing his role as David's caretaker. He told me stories about the years he and David had spent together, about the deep bond between the two of them and the love they'd shared. The scenario of a differently abled young man providing care for a sibling with even greater needs struck me not only as unusual, but deeply touching.

I came away from that meeting with the story of Aaron and David still warming my heart. I thought about the love they'd shared, the joy, the laughter, even the spiritual understanding. I thought about the comfort they had offered each other, and Aaron's uncanny sense that the two of them were "a pair." Both young men had been happy in their atypical lives. Even David, who couldn't speak, walk, or feed himself, had lived joyfully. While they had lived within different parameters than most of the population, their lives had been rich, filled with meaning. I believe the love and joy emanating from Aaron and David's relationship contributed to the wellbeing of the entire planet.

However, their story spoke to me in a specific way. After my brain injury robbed me of some of my capabilities, I had considered myself to be defective. Even though no one else in my life viewed me that way, I had begun thinking of myself as "half a person." Since my injury, I haven't had the stamina to socialize with others to the same extent that I used to. I am not as resilient as I used to be, and am easily derailed by stress. My cognitive challenges have slowed me down. My sensitivity to light doesn't allow me to be out in public as much as I'd like to be.

In fact, I've often asked myself, "If I can't live fully, why am I still here?"

But the story of Aaron and David made me realize that a meaningful life is available within whatever restrictions life imposes upon us. I can still live fully. Granted, unlimited opportunities are no longer available to me. The world is no longer wide open to me. But parts of it are, and within those parts, I can find a meaningful life. A valid life. A life that I can love.

I know another young man, Carl, who struggles with mental illness. He has difficulty connecting with people, but has a special affinity for animals. He does pet-sitting, and also cares for farm animals. I've been told he does an excellent job with his friends in the animal kingdom.

After a week of caring for the farm animals of a relative who'd gone on vacation, Carl gave me a detailed account of the behavior of barn cats. I'd never heard such a story. He described their peculiar habits, the nuances of their personality differences, the behavioral patterns of the leaders of the clan, and the responses of their followers. Most of us never observe the minute details of which Carl is keenly aware. It isn't just that we don't take the time. We don't have the capacity to view barnyard cat society through the special lens of Carl's perspective. While he, too, has an "out of the norm" brain, he finds enjoyment and satisfaction in his unique perspectives.   He enjoys valid life experiences.

Years ago, when I was working as a psychotherapist, I had a client named Sandra, a woman whose life had been profoundly altered by a stroke. She told me something a friend had said to her: "If this had happened to me, I would've committed suicide."

Sandra's eyes filled with pain when she recounted that story, and I understood why. Someone had suggested to her that she no longer had a life worth living. She knew that her life still had value, and she wanted others to recognize that fact.

As I came away from that meeting with Aaron, I felt something stirring inside me: a determination to find joy in my new life. *Can I find a new drumbeat?* I wondered. *A different rhythm of daily living that I can embrace with gratitude? Can I confidently march to that beat, letting it carry me where I need to go, even if I am out of step with those around me? Can I trust enough to surrender to the beat, to open myself to new perspectives, to receive the unique blessings they bring? Can I find a home on that different plane Aaron spoke of?*

The answer, I was sure, was *YES.* I knew it would take time, and a great deal of faith. But still, *YES.*

BE THOU MY VISION

In the early months after my brain injury, one of my doctors asked me a question: "If you could cure just one of your symptoms, which one would it be?"

I responded without hesitation. "My vision problems."

Without a doubt, the vision challenges resulting from my brain injury are the symptoms that create the most disruption in my life. I have been diagnosed with post-traumatic vision syndrome. Part of that syndrome is something called convergence insufficiency, which means that my eyes don't work properly together. They essentially see two different images that my brain has difficulty making sense of.

One of my optometrists offered me a detailed explanation of how this convergence problem resulted from the whiplash that occurred when I was struck by the car. Another doctor explained it in simpler terms: "When people get head injuries, their eyes don't line up right."

My convergence insufficiency is especially problematic for my near vision. It means that reading and any other type of close, visually intense work is difficult and painful. When I am tired or overstimulated, the problem becomes worse. It also worsens as the day progresses, which means that reading and close work become nearly impossible in the evening. When I overtax myself visually, I experience a brain strain that makes me feel both wildly agitated and deeply exhausted.

I often experience waves of nausea and dizziness that feel like motion sickness. These episodes can occur when I sweep my eyes from one point to another, or when I'm scanning a row of objects, such as merchandise in a store or books on a shelf. The episodes also happen when I've pushed my eyes too far with reading or close work.

When I am tired or overstimulated, even my distance vision can be problematic. Things around me start to seem confusing and surreal. Sometimes, I have what I call "visual meltdowns," where I can no longer make sense of anything I see.

Even when my brain is not under stress, I frequently miss seeing objects right in my line of vision. Here's a silly example of my visual incompetence. I habitually keep a bottle of hand lotion on the vanity next to my bathroom sink. A bottle of hair conditioner sits in the shower stall, along with my shampoo.

One day, I inadvertently switched the bottles of lotion and hair conditioner when I put them back into place after cleaning the bathroom. The only similarities between the two bottles were that they were both made of white plastic and had pump dispensers. They were shaped differently and were of different sizes. Obviously, they were labeled differently.

For days, I looked at these products sitting in the wrong locations, failing to spot the mistake I'd made. I pumped what I thought was lotion from the bottle by the sink and rubbed it on my arms and legs, all the while wondering why it was so runny and why it took so long to soak into my skin. After shampooing, I pumped what I thought was conditioner into my hand and tried to spread it through my hair, puzzled as to why it was so thick and gooey.

On the evening of the sixth day, the clouds of visual cluelessness finally parted, and I saw that the bottle sitting in the shower stall was labeled as lotion. Aghast, I turned to the vanity and saw the bottle of hair conditioner sitting there. I picked up the two bottles and carried them to the living room where my husband was sitting. Laughing, I confessed to him what I'd done.

Oddly, the two products had proven to be somewhat interchangeable. I was glad my grooming hadn't suffered too much that week.

My brain injury has also left me with photophobia, sensitivity to light.

Houses and public buildings are set up to accommodate people whose characteristics fall within certain norms. That means that a person with dwarfism is forced to function in a world where everything is out of reach. People with exceptional height or girth live in a world where things such as chairs, beds, and doorways are too small to accommodate their size.

I live in a world that is too bright. No public accommodations are made for those who suffer from photophobia. It is up to us to manage on our own.

I am constantly moving away from sources of light, finding

safety in the shadows. Bright sunlight is challenging enough, but artificial lighting is far more difficult to contend with. At home, I function by dipping in and out of light, doing as much of my housework as I can without turning on a light in the room. Sometimes, I turn on a light in an adjacent room, which provides sufficient illumination without exposing me directly to the light. I take a bath or shower in a dark bathroom, then turn on the lights at key points when doing my hair and makeup.

A few minutes under artificial lighting can be okay, but the longer I'm exposed to it, the more oppressive and unbearable it becomes. My ability to tolerate light decreases as the day passes.

It is hard to find words to describe what happens when I am exposed to too much light. I begin to feel sick, overwhelmed, and overstimulated. I am unable to focus or think clearly. As the situation progresses from bad to worse, I feel assaulted, tormented. At times when I've become completely overwrought from exposure to light, even a single flickering candle in the room is too much for me to bear. The only cure for my distress is the soothing effect of total darkness.

Shortly after my injury, when I was still confused and bewildered by my symptoms, my physical therapist pointed out that wearing sunglasses in lighted buildings would ease some of my discomfort. About three years later, I discovered a small thing that made a huge improvement in the quality of my life: wrap sunglasses. The lenses in wrap sunglasses shut out the light that comes through the sides of regular sunglasses. Wrap sunglasses enable me to spend more time in public buildings, and in lighted rooms in my own house. They have allowed me to take a few more steps toward living a normal life.

Once, someone said to me, "It would drive me crazy to wear sunglasses all the time." I winced at her suggestion that my life was unbearable. Wearing sunglasses hasn't driven me crazy. It is what I need to do, and I've adjusted to it.

However, even the darkest wrap lenses cannot provide all the protection I need. Even while wearing them, I still feel discomfort from prolonged exposure to artificial lighting. While in public, I often take breaks from the light by closing my eyes, my dark lenses concealing the fact that I am doing this. Although I wear my wrap sunglasses in church, I sit through much of the service with my eyes closed.

At times, I exercise at the gym with closed eyes. When I was attending my medical exercise program, I had friends who would wave at me from across the room. I had to explain to my friend Gloria that if I didn't respond to her wave, it wasn't because I was being snobbish. It was because I hadn't seen her, as I'd closed my eyes to take a break from the light.

In the years since my injury, I have finally figured out, through trial and error, what works best for me in terms of supportive eyewear. As of now, I have three different pairs of glasses.

I have my prescription wrap sunglasses, which I wear to shield myself from bright sunlight and artificial lighting. These are the glasses that most people see me wearing.

I have a pair of normal prescription glasses that I wear in daylight hours around the house. Instead of clear lenses, these glasses have grayish lenses, a tint more comfortable for my eyes. They take the edge off the glare of normal daylight.

Finally, I have a pair of glasses with yoking prism lenses. The prisms serve to bring my eyes' two separate images together into one image. I use my prism lenses for reading and other types of close work.

Without my prism lenses, many ordinary activities would be extraordinarily difficult for me, if not impossible. They allow me to sort through the mail, write out a shopping list, file my nails, thread a needle, and trim dead leaves off a house plant. These invaluable prism glasses have a set of sunglass lenses that adhere magnetically, so that they can easily be popped on or off. I use my prism glasses for writing, adding the sunglass lenses for protection against the intolerably bright computer screen.

All day long, I am constantly switching from regular glasses to sunglasses to prism glasses.

As grateful as I am for them, my prism lenses aren't magical. Even when I use them, I have limited stamina for reading and close work. It seems as if I have a certain amount of eye-power allotted for each day, and that small amount must be budgeted.

Prior to my injury, my lifestyle was oriented toward visually intense activities: reading, working on the computer, artwork, sewing. Now, to keep from exhausting my eyes and overstimulating my brain, I need to intersperse visually intense activities with other activities. If I overrun my allotted close-work time for the day, I plunge myself into exhaustion, emotional agitation, and cognitive confusion. Through many such unfortunate experiences, I have learned that it is best to pay attention to my limitations.

By the end of the day, my eye-power is completely spent, which means I run out of things to do to pass the time. This is especially true in the winter, when the weather keeps me indoors. Since I can't read in the evenings, I turn to television. But even though I wear sunglasses to protect myself from the brightness of the screen, watching too much TV strains my eyes. Thus, every evening, I am forced to get creative.

When I think of this dilemma as something that will last for the rest of my life, I become profoundly discouraged. So, I try to view it as a one-day-at-a-time problem, with a one-day-at-a-time solution, something that needs to be solved anew every evening.

One obvious answer to running out of things to do at the end of the day is to spend time in meditation. This activity involves no visual strain, and brings nothing but positive results. Developing the discipline to engage in daily meditation is something I continue to work on.

Writing may seem like a strange occupation for someone with vision problems. Every day, I question why I keep on writing when the visual work involved causes me so much pain. It is only because of my passion for writing that I continue to struggle through the difficulties. I don't know what I'd do to fill the hole in my life if I stopped writing.

The initial phase of a writing project is onerous for me, as it involves sorting my notes and pounding out a first draft. It tends to be a frustrating and confusing process, not only visually, but cognitively as well. The strain can bring me to tears.

The second phase of writing is the reason I put up with the stress of the first phase. Once I have the bare bones in place, fleshing out my stories is pure pleasure. As I spend most of my day in solitude, my fictional characters become the companions who alleviate my loneliness. I love delving into the hearts and minds of my "imaginary friends," observing what they do, listening to their conversations, and then recording it all in a book. Even though visually taxing, this part of the writing process is addictive for me. Creating stories calms my agitated mind and soothes my troubled emotions.

I do my writing on my computer. However, I cannot work for too long before my eyes and my brain give out. I reach a point where I can no longer make sense of what I'm doing, and am forced to stop. So, I work on my projects in bits and pieces.

This "bits and pieces" process continues throughout my day, even when I'm away from my computer in my upstairs writing room. The story continues to roll along in my mind, a phenomenon I call "head-writing." I keep pieces of scrap paper, cut to the size of notecards, stacked in a basket in my dining room. When I'm working on some household task, I frequently get an idea for my writing project. I stop what I'm doing, grab a scrap of paper, scribble down my idea, and toss it into a second basket that I keep in the stairwell. Periodically, the contents of this basket get taken upstairs and incorporated into my work at the computer.

Taking twenty seconds to scribble down a sudden inspiration doesn't task my vision too much, and allows me to stay with my project all day long. I also keep paper in my handbag so that I can record ideas when I'm away from the house. When I come back home, there is often a "putting away" ritual—my coat, car keys, groceries, receipts—that also includes removing the writing ideas from my bag and putting them in the stairwell basket.

It seems that the minute I get up from my computer and trudge down the stairs, telling myself I'm done writing for the day, I'm flooded with ideas. The basket that just got emptied on my trip up the stairs begins to fill up again.

I've joked with my husband that exposure to water seems to trigger head-writing, as ideas invariably come to me in the shower or bathtub. Almost without fail, I dash out of the bathroom wrapped in a towel so that I can grab a scrap of paper to record my thoughts. If it wasn't for the risk of electrocution, a remedy for writer's block could be sitting at your computer with your feet in a tub of water. Perhaps a better solution would be to

17

take paper and pencil and sit on a log beside a stream, allowing the current to wash over your dangling feet.

Thankfully, I now have a few adaptations in place that help to compensate for my visual challenges associated with writing. Several years after my injury, I became a client of Michigan Rehabilitation Services (MRS). That agency has provided me with a desktop computer with an enormous screen, so that I no longer need to peer at the small screen of my laptop computer. When writing, I increase the font to a size that would seem ridiculous to anyone else. Working with large print creates less of a convergence problem for my eyes.

MRS has also provided me with a lighted keyboard, which means I don't need to turn on any lights in the room when I write. Additionally, they've given me a voice recognition program. I use this program for the initial draft of a passage, when accuracy is not yet critical. This gives me a break from staring at the computer screen. I've discovered that typing a first draft with my eyes closed also works.

Editing, the final stage of writing, is a brutal process for me. While I always use the spelling and grammar check, it fails to detect every mistake. The strain of closely scrutinizing my work becomes unbearable. I can't trust my wayward eyes to catch errors, and this creates a great deal of anxiety for me.

All the adaptations I use when I work on the computer fly out the window when it is time to edit a proof copy of a book in paper form. The grueling process turns me into an emotional mess. Thankfully, my husband helps with checking a final draft for errors.

My friend Roseanne has, on occasion, served as an informal editor, reading my manuscripts and giving me feedback. She is a quilt-maker with keen eyesight who can work all day on her craft. She sometimes tells me that she reads my books in one or two sittings. This astounds me, as it takes me up to two weeks to read one of my own books in paper form. Even then, I'm almost out of my mind from the visual strain.

Needless to say, my days of reading for pleasure are a thing of the past. No longer can I curl up with a book in the evening and lose myself in it for hours on end. Reading is no longer a hobby. It has become a painful chore.

Before my injury, I had pictured my retirement years as a time when I would read everything I'd never had time to read before. I'd been eager to study subjects of particular interest to me: philosophy, religion, classical literature, art history, world history. I had wanted to take courses in math, physics, and art. I had wanted to explore naturopathic medicine, and to learn more about energy healing.

But delving into study during my retirement years isn't the way things have turned out for me.

I do belong to a book club associated with my church. I read our group's selections on my electronic reader, adjusting the font to a large setting. But the glare of the electronic screen still bothers me. Rather than being a joy, the reading is a tedious process. Thankfully, our group reads only a short selection per week.

My reading comprehension has also suffered since my injury, although using my prism lenses helps. When my eyes and brain begin to tire, I can't comprehend even my own writing.

At times, I have listened to audiobooks from my local library. The problem with listening to books on CDs is that the discs are often scratched, which means I miss out on portions of the story. Also, scanning the titles of audiobooks on the library shelves is a torturous visual task. Several times, I have taken my husband to the library with me to help in the selection process.

Most people aren't aware of the fact that reading is painful for me. When I'm in a group of people who are discussing the latest best seller they've read, I experience a few moments of grief. One day when I was checking out audiobooks at the library, the librarian pointed me to a brochure and cheerfully asked if I'd like to participate in their summer reading program.

I shook my head. She looked at me curiously, as if unable to fathom a reason why I wouldn't want to join.

"No, thank you," I said. I walked out of the library overwhelmed with sadness.

My husband and I occasionally have appointments with bankers, financial advisors, and insurance agents. Inevitably, the person we are meeting with places a packet of information in front of me, always in fine print. As I appear to be a normal adult, they assume that I am capable of reading and comprehending the material they've handed me. The ensuing moment of embarrassment has now become commonplace for me, something I've become accustomed to. Fortunately, Russ jumps in at such times, serving as my eyes, taking the lead in the conversation.

My husband often serves as my eyes. That is one way his role in our marriage has been altered by my injury. He reads important documents and explains their contents to me. Sometimes, we sit down together while he reads the documents aloud to me.

While I am able to use the internet for a few minutes at a time, my husband does complicated searches for me. He completes most of the computer tasks associated with publishing and marketing my books.

When we shop together, he often finds items I am looking for. I do most of my clothing shopping alone, as I don't want to subject him to my nit-picky process of trying on twenty different garments before making a selection. But several winters ago, when I set out on the daunting quest for the perfect winter coat, I asked him to come along to help me. He read the labels describing cleaning instructions and what level of protection each coat would provide against a cold Michigan winter. About the time when my eyes were shot and my brain was melting down, he was able to keep the process going, calmly pulling out options for me to try on.

Several months after my injury, I talked with one of my rehab therapists about my difficulty with finding items in stores. I told her I'd confined my shopping to a handful of stores that I knew well: one store for groceries, another for pharmacy needs, and several others for clothing.

She shot me a disbelieving look. "But you can't confine your shopping to those few stores for the rest of your life," she said.

Inwardly, I disagreed with her. Walking down familiar aisles, where I know the location of all the products, certainly makes my life easier.

But that isn't always possible. Occasionally, I am forced to veer off my well-trod path to make a purchase in an unfamiliar store. On an unforgettable day in the summer of 2016, I had to muster the courage to enter a fabric store.

In the past, I did a lot of sewing. Frugal mother that I was, I made cute outfits for my young children from any scrap of fabric I could get my hands on. I made clothing for myself as well. When I was married to my second husband, our social life revolved around dancing. I spent hours at my sewing machine, creating fabulous dance dresses for myself, along with matching shirts for my husband.

Given my visual challenges, such creative projects are no longer a part of my life. I threw out my broken-down sewing machine years ago. However, there are occasional sewing projects that I need to do: reattach a button, mend a seam, repair a hem. In such cases, I gear up for the task by donning my prism glasses.

Nearly thirty ago when I was single, I traveled with a friend to Las Cruces, New Mexico. While there, we crossed the border into Mexico, where we browsed in shops. He bought me a beautiful skirt, which I wore for two or three years before it found its way into the back of my closet. It hung there for several decades, forlorn and unremembered. Every time I cleaned out my closet, I would think about getting rid of it. But I would decide not to, as the skirt held sentimental value for me.

When I pulled out the skirt in the summer of 2016, I decided I wanted to get some use out of it again. Sadly, I found it to be unwearable, as the elastic in the waistband had completely given out. So, I decided to tackle the project of putting on a new waistband and inserting new elastic. I would need to do all the sewing by hand, which I knew would be a daunting project.

And, it meant that I would need to step outside the bounds of my handful of well-known stores, to venture into a fabric store to buy supplies.

When I stepped through the door of the unfamiliar store, the endless aisles of colorful displays threw me into a daze. Everything around me seemed surreal. It felt as if I was standing in the middle of a Salvador Dali painting. I had no idea which aisle held the items I needed for my project.

I wandered up and down the aisles, unable to find what I wanted, becoming more overwhelmed and confused by the minute. Nothing made sense to me. My eyes were definitely not working together. They'd completely taken leave of each other, each happily doing their own thing.

Repeatedly, I approached store employees and asked, "Can you tell me where I can find the elastic?" Each time, the person glanced up from what she was doing and rattled off instructions I could not understand. Off I'd go again, wandering in circles, searching in vain.

After my third request for help, I finally found the display I was looking for. Feeling completely spent, I took my purchases up to the register, trying to hold onto my last ounce of sanity and my last shred of dignity. I couldn't wait to get out to my car, where I could take a few moments to pull myself together before embarking on the trip home.

Not knowing anything was amiss, the kindly cashier rang up my products. Then she asked, "Do you get our email coupons?"

I shook my head.

"Would you like to sign up for them?" she asked.

I made the mistake of saying, "Sure."

She whipped out a form for me to complete and placed it on the counter in front of me. It was short, just a dozen lines on a page, but it might as well have been a five-hundred-page document. I was mortified. I knew my eyes and brain were too far gone to be able to manage the reading and writing involved with answering a few simple questions. Not wanting to reveal my inadequacy, I said, "I'll do it another time."

"Are you sure?" the cashier said. "It won't take long." She had no idea that, at that moment, I was functionally illiterate.

I declined a second time before leaving the store, exhausted and on the verge of tears.

After experiences like this, I ask myself the question, "What could I have done differently to prevent this agonizing meltdown?" The only answer I can come up with is to have my husband accompany me on such ventures. He has no trouble orienting himself to strange surroundings, and his eagle eyes could spot a packet of elastic a mile away. Had he been with me, we would have been in and out of that store in three minutes, sparing me a world of pain.

Wearing my prism lenses, I managed to sew a new waistband on the lovely skirt my friend had bought me. I had to do it in multiple installments. Although the results weren't perfect, I was able to wear the skirt again.

But I paid a big price for taking on that project. Not only did I experience terrible eyestrain, but for the rest of that day and the following day, my brain felt weird, exhausted, and overtaxed. I felt emotionally out of kilter, as if I'd been through a traumatic event.

One morning at my book club, I sat with other group members in the church lounge, admiring a print of Seurat's *A Sunday Afternoon* on *the Island of La Grande Jatte* that recently had been hung in the room. I commented on how much I'd always liked that painting.

"You should see the real thing in the art museum in Chicago," one of the ladies said.

A wave of grief washed over me. I knew full well what would happen if I went on such an excursion. "I don't do museums well," I told her.

"Oh, yes," she said, remembering my brain injury.

Throughout my adult years of living in northern Indiana and southwestern Michigan, Chicago has been the nearest big city, just a two-hour drive from my home. Prior to my injury, I had occasionally taken daytrips to Chicago to visit the museums there. Now, I would love nothing more than to spend an entire day browsing through the magnificent works in the Art Institute.

But such an outing is no longer available to me. It is a part of the world that has been shut off to me. Not only would spending a day in a lighted building, with crowds of people milling around me, be a torturous experience, gazing at one work of art after another would become visually painful. In about half an hour, I would feel so sick that I would need to leave.

Several years ago, a friend invited me to go with her to a display of a local artist's work. Spending time with my friend was sweet, but gazing at paintings for twenty minutes was decidedly painful.

Prior to incurring my brain injury, I enjoyed oil painting and sculpting as hobbies. I did a little bit of sculpting in the first few years after my injury. But I have since given up that hobby, as sculpting now involves far more visual pain than pleasure. I have not even attempted to resume oil painting.

A new trend for promoting relaxation is coloring books for adults. Several years before my injury, when I was working a high-pressure job, I purchased a trio of such books containing intricate mandala designs. Coloring the designs did, indeed, prove to be an effective technique for calming my agitated mind. However, when I turned to coloring to settle my post-injury nerves, I found the activity to be stressful for my brain, rather than soothing. The longer I would color, the more agitated I would feel.

One day at Tai Chi, one of the class members passed out invitations to a Zentangle party at her house. The card she handed me said, *Zentangle is an easy to learn, relaxing, and fun way to create beautiful images by drawing structured patterns.*

The pre-injury me would have loved Zentangle. I felt a pull of attraction to the activity before reality sank in. I knew that if I went to that party, I'd get partway through the activity before having a visual meltdown and being forced to quit. I'd have to explain to a group of bewildered strangers why I was behaving so weirdly. I thanked the woman for her invitation, knowing her activity was off limits for me.

My mother never drove much in her adult life, only when my father was not available to take her where she needed to go. She never developed much confidence behind the wheel of a car. Early in her senior years, she narrowly missed having an accident. "That's it," she said. "I'm not driving anymore."

I was disappointed, as I thought she'd given up too easily. I judged her for not trying harder. She hadn't waited for her children to take her car keys away when she was eighty-five or ninety. She voluntarily handed them over several decades earlier.

But here I am, just as uncomfortable with driving as she was back then. Because I've had so many near-misses since my brain injury, I drive as little as possible. I rarely drive with a passenger in the car, as I don't want to put anyone else at risk.

I've had a number of visual meltdowns while driving, where I've become visually disoriented and unable to make sense of my surroundings. Obviously, this is dangerous. So, for the most part, I limit my driving to short trips around town, for appointments, shopping, or other errands.

I have learned from experience that I can, on rare occasions, drive for as long as an hour, but only if the route is familiar and if it doesn't involve city driving. Traffic lights and headlights overstimulate my brain, making me feel disoriented.

But even if I succeed in driving an hour's distance from my home, getting back home is always a problem. I am inevitably too tired to make the return trip without putting myself through a great deal of strain.

On my birthday in November 2016, my son Quinton arrived at my house to take me out for dinner. As he was unfamiliar with my vehicle, I broke my own rule about driving with a passenger in the car, and drove the two of us five miles to a local Chinese restaurant.

Our dinner conversation was intense and animated. By the time we left the restaurant, I was exhausted and overstimulated. I knew I was rapidly spiraling into a brain meltdown. I was in no condition to drive, and did not want to endanger my passenger.

So, even though he'd never driven my car before, I asked Quinton to drive us home. He had to orient himself to all the unfamiliar controls: headlights, windshield wipers, turn signals, seat adjustments. My failure humiliated me, but I knew that by relinquishing the wheel, I'd done the right thing. We made it home safely.

When I look back on how I judged my mother for so easily giving up on driving, I feel remorseful. Now, I can identify with how vulnerable she must have felt.

As if post-traumatic vision syndrome was not a big enough problem, several years after my injury I was visited with a second vision challenge. In late summer 2015, as I was attempting to edit one of my books, I realized I was struggling harder than I had with previous books.

What's going on? I wondered. *Is there something else wrong with my eyes?*

I scheduled an appointment with my optometrist. To my astonishment, he informed me that I now had cataracts in both eyes. Not just one type of cataract, but two. The cataract that had been in my right eye for decades had grown, and the same kind was now developing in my left eye as well. Additionally, I had the beginnings of age-associated cataracts in both eyes.

My optometrist referred me to an eye surgeon, who determined that I was a candidate for cataract removal surgery. Over a series of appointments, I had tests and procedures done in preparation for the surgery.

Many people dread going to the dentist because of the painful and intrusive nature of dental work. Given a choice, I'd take a dental appointment any day over seeing an eye doctor. I'd actually prefer having a colonoscopy to seeing an eye doctor. I hate having bright lights shined in my eyes. And I detest having my eyes dilated so that the doctor can peer deep inside them.

At each of my pre-surgery appointments and post-surgery checkups, my eyes had to be dilated. The procedure began to feel like a routine torture. It seemed to me that each time my eyes were dilated, they took a little longer to return to normal. Thus, I was spending entire days with surreal vision, something that created considerable misery for me.

My husband accompanied me to all these appointments so that he could drive me home after my eyes had been dilated. But, due to miscommunication with the clinic staff, there came an appointment when I was under the impression that my eyes were not going to be dilated that day. So, I gave my husband a break from his chauffeuring duties and happily drove myself to the appointment.

I was wrong, of course. The minute I sat down in the examination chair, the optometrist's assistant administered drops to dilate my eyes, just as she'd done at all my previous visits. And there I was, stuck at the clinic with impaired vision, with no one available to drive me home.

Panic took hold of me. I knew that if the doctor's staff became aware of my plight, they would insist that I stay at the clinic until my vision returned to normal. I didn't want to tell them that, due to my eyes' slowness in recovering from dilation, such an order would mean that I'd need to camp out in the waiting room for the rest of the day. I imagined the pitiful scenario of curling up in a corner long after the staff had gone home, waiting until my husband finished his second-shift job at 11:00 PM and came to get me.

I just wanted to get home, to recuperate from my intrusive eye procedures in privacy. Like a sneaky child, I slipped out of the clinic and sat in my car, trying to decide what to do. I called my husband and wailed to him about my predicament, hoping he could come and help me. But he wasn't in a position where he could leave work and run to my assistance.

So, I did something I never should have done. I decided to go against all reason and drive myself home. I went down the back roads as much as possible, so that I would have less traffic to contend with. When I finally had to join the traffic in town, I kept a death grip on the steering wheel, peering through crazy eyes at the weird, wild road in front of me. All the while, I prayed fervently, "Just let me make it home. Just let me make it home." Thankfully, I suffered no mishaps.

I need to inject a note of caution here, as is done in television shows where outrageous stunts are performed. *Don't do this at home! Never do what I did!*

Because what I did was highly dangerous. Now, I make every effort to avoid such a predicament. I take it for granted that my eyes will be dilated every time I visit the optometrist, and I schedule those appointments for times when my husband can go with me.

As anyone who has undergone cataract surgery knows, there is a period of two or three months when your vision is a mess. The new, artificial lens inserted into your eye changes your vision, so that the old prescription in your glasses no longer works for you. One eye is operated on at a time, and that one must recover sufficiently before the second surgery is attempted. Then your eyes need to stabilize for four to six weeks before your prescription needs can be assessed.

My surgeries took place in mid-November and early December. For two and a half miserable months, I struggled through my daily activities without proper glasses. I'd put on my old glasses for near vision tasks, but would have to take them off immediately because they distorted my distance vision. This misery extended through the Christmas season, and I attempted holiday preparations in a state of profound visual impairment. I endured numerous brain meltdowns resulting from visual strain. When I tried baking Christmas cookies, seven-layer bars, they ended up with only six layers, as my frustrated eyes skipped over the part of the recipe that instructed me to add nuts.

Going through the multiple challenges associated with eye surgery seemed like adding insult to my already injured vision. When I finally received my new glasses in January, it felt as if I'd been bestowed with the world's greatest gift.

However, over the following year, I realized that my post-surgery glasses didn't fully meet my needs. So, in early 2017, I once again headed out to purchase eyewear. I was confident that I'd figured out exactly what I wanted. While my eye exams and surgeries are performed at a clinic that offers comprehensive care for complex vision problems, I take my prescriptions to be filled at a different clinic, one that offers frames and lenses at a less expensive rate.

Unfortunately, my confident quest quickly ran into roadblocks. First, I had to deal with a communication snafu between my exam clinic and the clinic where I purchase my glasses. After taking a few days to straighten this out, I sat down with an optician at the glasses clinic to explain what I needed. He listened to what I said, then offered a new option he believed would solve my problem with the brightness of the computer screen. He told me it had worked wonders for him.

Of course, I wanted to believe in his magical cure, and I agreed to his suggestion. But when I picked up my new glasses a few days later, I discovered that his suggestion had made matters with the computer worse, rather than better, for me. So, I trudged back to the clinic, reported the problem, and put in a new order for glasses.

Three times, for various reasons, I picked up glasses that were wrong for me. Each time, I had to take them back and place a new order.

This confusing process stretched out for three weeks. I walked in and out of the clinic more than a dozen times. I'm sure the staff grew tired of seeing me coming, saying to each other, "What's her problem now?" My anxiety and despair mounted with each unsuccessful visit and each frustrating conversation. I berated myself for the breakdown in communication, and for ending up in such a muddle.

Once again, I spent weeks fumbling through my daily activities without the proper prescription. My entire life felt out of control. Toward the end of the process, I found myself on the verge of caving in to despair and resigning myself to wearing the wrong prescription. But a voice of reason prevailed in my mind, and I drove back to the clinic to make one last attempt at sorting out the problem.

When the issue was finally resolved and I had my new glasses in hand, I sang for joy. The clinic received a very nice thank you note from me, praising their customer service and their patience.

Despite all my vision difficulties, it is important to remind myself that most of the world of visual enjoyment is still open to me. There are still many things I can gaze at with pleasure. The spider plant with its cascade of babies hanging in my bedroom window. The maple tree in my front yard that turns flaming red every autumn, contrasting with the birch trees in the side yard that turn yellow. The winter trees with their intricate branches starkly outlined against the overcast sky. The squirrels, rabbits, chipmunks, and endless species of birds feasting on seeds on my backyard patio. The tall garden angel statue that watches over all these creatures. The tiny angel statues perched on my bookshelves, gifts from family and friends. The smile of the elderly immigrant woman who passes by my house on her daily walk, her friendly wave compensating for her difficulty with the English language. The fabulous, colorful outfits hanging in the window of the costume shop down the street from my home. The sunlight pouring through the stained-glass windows in my church. The faces of my husband, my children, my friends. I am profoundly grateful that I can see all this.

I attend an Episcopal church not far from my home. One Sunday in late 2016, we sang one of my favorite hymns, *Be Thou*

My Vision. That morning, the song struck me in a new way. I realized the title of that hymn held three lovely meanings that pertain to my vision.

The simplest meaning was one that hit close to home. Nearly every day, I make a *Be Thou My Vision* request of my husband. "Will you find this for me?" "Will you read this to me?" "Will you check to see if I've done this correctly?" "Will you look this up on the internet for me?" I never doubt that such acts of kindness on his part are wrapped in a great deal of love.

Secondly, the word *vision* is associated with seeing something that isn't normally perceived by the human eye. As I sing the hymn, I am saying to the divine, "When I am visited by a vision, let it be your glorious presence that I see."

The third meaning of *Be Thou My Vision* pertains to asking God to look at things and interpret them for me, just as I do with my husband. But this request is to help me see the conditions of my life from a higher perspective. To allow me to see my challenges through spiritual eyes, rather than through my limited human perception.

I ask the divine to help me see myself as more than a person with a traumatic brain injury. I ask to be lifted to a higher vantage point, from which I can view all the dimensions of my life, including those I cannot see now.

GUIDE MY FOOTSTEPS

In the immediate aftermath of my brain injury, I struggled with a very odd gait problem. While I had moments of walking normally, much of the time my gait was jerky and shuffling. One day when I almost fell in my doctor's office, he decided it was time to send me to physical therapy.

Hobbling into the physical therapy clinic was one of the lowest points in my life. I could not fathom how I had been reduced to such a condition. I was sure all eyes were on me as I approached the reception desk with my jerky shuffle. I imagined people were whispering to each other, "What in the world is wrong with that woman?"

Thankfully, physical therapy helped. Using the pointers my therapist had given me, I practiced my gait at home. Within a few months, I was walking normally—that is, most of the time.

Unfortunately, I couldn't prevent my gait problem from flaring up again in situations where I experienced stress or sensory overload. I could walk up to the door of a public building with a perfect gait. But upon encountering the overstimulating environment inside the building, my gait would fail me, the jerky shuffle taking over again.

Now, more than seven years later, that lurching gait seems to be a thing of the past. However, a shadow of that old problem still darkens my path. At times when I experience sensory or mental overload, my gait becomes slow and wobbly. If I overtax my eyes by writing for too long, I get up from my computer and hobble down the stairs like a debilitated old woman.

At such times, every step is a supreme effort. It feels as if I am trying to make my way through knee-deep mud.

Several winters ago, I went shopping for gloves at a local mall. I frequently shop at the two large stores at each end of the mall, but rarely go inside the mall. That day, I wanted to compare prices on gloves in those two stores. Instead of getting in my car and driving from one end of the mall to the other, I decided to walk through the mall.

I immediately regretted my decision. The unfamiliar sights, sounds, and scents of the interior of the mall quickly overstimulated my brain. My surroundings dissolved into a surreal blur. Despite my greatest effort, my gait slowed to a snail's pace. The walk between the two stores seemed interminable.

A month later, my husband and I entered a local lamp store, a quaint "mom and pop" establishment filled with interesting and unusual products. I'd never shopped there before, so everything was new to me. While I wanted to enjoy the adventure, scanning the merchandise overwhelmed my senses. Again, my gait failed me, and my husband had to help me out of the store.

Russ is familiar with my gait relapses. He thinks I move like Frankenstein's monster during those episodes, and has given me the nickname of "Franken-mommy." The term has become a code word for us. If my gait begins to fail me when we're out in public together, he says something along the lines of, "Okay, you're becoming Franken-mommied. We need to leave now." He knows to reach for my hand or offer me his arm to steady me. My normal gait quickly reasserts itself when I leave the challenging situation.

Not only does overstimulation affect my gait, it also affects the use of my hands, rendering them weak and clumsy. This often happens when I am out in public. In such situations, starting the zipper on my coat becomes a difficult task. To avoid this scenario, I tried to find a zipper-free winter coat, but was unable to do so.

When in a store, I am always exhausted from the strain of shopping by the time I enter the checkout line. My fumbling hands make it difficult to handle coupons and retrieve credit cards from my wallet. I feel embarrassed about how slow I am when it comes to completing transactions with the cashier.

One day when I was standing in the pharmacy checkout line, doing my usual fumbling routine, the man behind me seemed impatient. In a testy voice, he requested that a second register be opened. I was pretty sure he was aggravated by my slowness.

I remembered how, years earlier, I'd been the impatient one, irritated by the slowness of elderly people in checkout lines. Sadly, I remembered vowing that I never would become that much of a nuisance.

Don't do this, I mentally communicated to the impatient man. *You never know what a person is struggling with. In a split second, you could be in my condition.*

Just as I experienced a subsequent vision crisis after being diagnosed with post-traumatic vision syndrome, I experienced a second daunting chapter in the saga of my gait. The first time, the problem had to do with the injury to my brain. The second time, the issue resided in my spine.

I have a lengthy history of back problems. In the early 1990s, when my job as a social worker required a great deal of driving, the long hours of sitting behind the wheel of the car produced my first experience of lumbar pain. From that point on, I became a regular fixture in the waiting room of my chiropractor's office.

Periodically, my chronic low-grade problem would give way to episodes of excruciating pain. The muscle spasms during those episodes would contort my body into something resembling a letter C, with my right shoulder dipping and my right hip jutting out.

At one point, my chiropractor sent me for an MRI, which revealed that I had a bulging disc in my lumbar spine. Regular spinal adjustments, along with back exercises, seemed to be the only way to manage this condition.

I struggled on, suffering debilitating episodes of severe back pain once every year or two. Certainly, being hit by a car didn't help the matter. But that accident was not the origin of the problem.

In the summer of 2014, my husband and I embarked upon a four-hour road trip to a family reunion in southern Indiana. The prolonged sitting in the car aggravated my lumbar problem, and soon after we returned home, I went to see my chiropractor.

But this time, chiropractic treatment failed to alleviate my symptoms. Something was different about the pain this time. It radiated down the side of my right leg in a way that made walking agonizing. As with previous episodes, my posture became bent and twisted. The pain worsened as the weeks passed.

I finally went to see my primary care physician, who referred me to an orthopedic physical therapy clinic. Once again, I found myself hobbling into a therapy facility humiliated by my impaired gait. I received several months of treatment, but saw no relief from symptoms.

For years, I had taken long outdoor walks as a form of exercise. As my back and leg pain worsened, it became harder and harder to even walk the distance of half a block. My physical therapist told me to stop. "You are just making things worse," he said.

The loss of my ability to take a walk, a much-cherished activity that I'd fought to regain after my brain injury, felt like death to me. Being visited by a gait problem a second time seemed like an unfair punishment.

Is this the end of my ability to walk normally? I wondered. *Will I need to accept life in this compromised condition?*

"What am I going to do if I can't take my walks?" I asked my physical therapist. "I'm afraid I'm going to lose all my muscle strength."

Sympathetic to my plight, he helped me sign up for the medical exercise program associated with the physical therapy clinic. He directed me to work out on a seated elliptical machine, so that I could get a cardio workout while keeping my limbs moving. At that point, I was in such poor shape that six or seven minutes on that machine was all I could manage.

As my condition deteriorated, I could barely walk across a room. I couldn't stand for more than a few minutes to do any household chore. Negotiating the stairs to my upstairs writing room or to my basement laundry room became a daunting task. I could no longer keep up with the work in my flowerbeds. I began to think that my days in my house were numbered, and that my husband and I would be forced to move to an apartment where I wouldn't need to contend with stairs or yardwork.

Then something serendipitous happened. I met a woman at church who'd recently had back surgery performed by a local neurosurgeon, Dr. Simons. She told me the procedure had done wonders for her.

My husband and I did some research on Dr. Simons. We learned that he was known for his brilliance in performing high-tech back surgery, much less intrusive than old surgical techniques. This allowed his patients a much shorter and easier recovery time. I talked with my physical therapist about Dr. Simons, and he suggested that I set up an appointment with him.

I had to go through a lengthy, convoluted process of getting a proper referral to Dr. Simons. At one point, I was told that he had a long list of people waiting for surgery, and that he was scheduled out for about four months. I had no idea how I would survive waiting that long in my condition.

As I counted down the days until I could see the doctor, cold winter weather set in, the daylight hours becoming shorter and shorter. Around that time, my husband moved from first shift to second shift at his job, which left me alone during the long, dark evenings.

Everything about my life felt like a descent into darkness. It seemed as if the cold, the darkness, the loneliness, and the excruciating pain all became one thing. I wondered whether I had reached a point of permanent darkness and debilitation in my life. But I knew that something about the situation would change. Until then, I had to go through this very difficult passage.

I was required to get an MRI of my back before I could even see Dr. Simons. When I read the report of the MRI in my online medical chart, I was astounded to learn that I had a herniated disc in my lumbar spine. It was the same disc that had been noted to be bulging twenty years earlier.

When I finally succeeded in obtaining an appointment with the surgeon, he showed me images from the MRI. Pointing to the part of the faulty disc that was protruding and impinging on a nerve, he said, "There's your guy."

Inwardly, I laughed. I should have known all along that the aberration in my spine causing me so much pain was of the male gender!

Dr. Simons apparently considered my condition to be an emergency, as I was not placed on a waiting list. My surgery was promptly scheduled for a week later, in mid-December 2014.

Finally, the long-awaited day arrived when my husband drove me to our local hospital for the surgery. High-tech procedure that it was, I needed no hospitalization afterwards, and was sent home late in the afternoon. Despite the post-surgery pain, I immediately noticed an improvement in my ability to walk.

That evening, I made repeated trips to stand in front of the full-length mirror in my bedroom, watching in amazement as, hour by hour, my twisted body unwound and straightened. It was the first time I'd been able to stand up straight in almost half a year. I was overjoyed to see my old self again. As I still had traces of anesthesia in my system, my drug-addled brain experienced the unfolding as euphoric.

The following day, still in my post-anesthesia mind-altered state, I recorded the following in my journal, a letter to the hospital staff which, thankfully, was never sent to them.

I wish to express my warmest regards and deepest appreciation to Dr. Simons and his surgical staff, who took such wonderful care of me during my surgery on December 15, 2014. Five months prior to my surgery, I had entered a dark tunnel of pain that sapped my strength and threatened to extinguish all hope, contorting my suffering body into the shape of a bent and twisted old woman.

Thank you to all those who, during my prep for surgery, made damn sure that I wasn't an imposter by repeatedly asking me my name, my date of birth, and the nature of my surgery. I trust that by the end of the day, you were all convinced that I was the bona fide Lois Jean Thomas.

A special thanks to the person who put the good stuff in my IV bag, the drug that made me giggle so hard that I could barely utter my vital information the umpteenth time it was requested of me.

Thank you to the person who wheeled me down the hallway to the operating room. Making that trip is the last of my pre-surgery memories. This baffles me. Surely, I entered the operating room wide awake. Surely, I must have come face-to-face with an anesthesiologist, who undoubtedly conversed with me before ushering me into oblivion.

Kind anesthesiologist, this lost time troubles me. I feel like a drunk unable to recall the previous night's foolishness. If I spoke or behaved in any unseemly manner, I beg your forgiveness. And thank you for watching over me, bringing me through the surgery and back into consciousness with no ill effects other than a scratchy throat.

When my eyes fluttered open in the recovery room, I gazed in confusion at the hazy forms surrounding me. I moved my hand to my face and realized that someone, mindful of my photophobia, had put my protective dark glasses back on me. Attending nurse, I thank you for that.

Out of nowhere, a surgeon-shaped apparition popped up at the foot of my bed. "Your surgery went very well," it sang out in a cheerful voice. I breathed a sigh of relief, thankful that I hadn't been maimed or mutilated during the operation. The phantom asked me to wiggle my toes. Satisfied by my performance, it vanished into the nothingness from whence it had sprung.

Thank you, thank you, phantom surgeon, for implementing a procedure that produced near-miraculous results. It seems that an ill-tempered critter with razor sharp teeth had taken up lodging in the space between my fourth and fifth lumbar vertebrae. Whenever I moved my body in a way that displeased him, he chomped down on a nearby nerve. You deftly plucked him out through an incision half the length of a matchstick.

Thank you to the kind nurse in the second recovery room who gave me a much-needed spa treatment. You helped me out of bed and into a chair, then wrapped me like an Egyptian mummy in heated flannel blankets. When it was time to go home, I was loath to leave my cozy cocoon.

At home, as the anesthesia fog lingered, I was visited by a post-surgical state of expanded awareness. My new consciousness had something to do with all of us blundering earthly souls offering our best to the wellbeing of the planet, raising our quavering voices in an anthem of praise to the God of beauty, truth, and goodness. In taking care of me before, during, and after my surgery, you were all singing your part in the universal song.

As the evening hours passed, I watched my bent and twisted body unfurl. I could hardly tear myself away from the full-length mirror, as I couldn't stop admiring the straightness of my form.

From the bottom of my heart, I thank you all for the help you've given me. My lumbar spine thanks you. The nerve in my right leg thanks you. Its anguished cry of pain has been replaced by a veritable song of joy.

May God bless all of you as you continue to lift your voices in the cosmic choir.

Truly, my gratitude in the aftermath of my surgery knew no bounds. Once again, I had overcome a gait problem. While the impingement of the herniated disc on the nerve in my leg created some permanent damage, I regained my full mobility. I am now able to garden again, and to negotiate stairs without a problem. The nerve becomes agitated from time to time, demanding to be babied. But it does not interfere with my activities.

A month after my back surgery, I resumed my participation in the medical exercise program with new resolve. I transitioned from the seated elliptical to the treadmill and the standing elliptical, along with a variety of weight machines. One of the clinic's physical therapists was assigned the role of evaluating and coaching the medical exercise participants, and she helped me design an appropriate exercise regimen. The warm, supportive environment in the clinic made me feel secure.

Many of the members of the medical exercise program had serious health problems. Compared to them, I felt most fortunate.

As so much traffic flowed in and out of that clinic, I made up a game of spotting celebrity look-alikes. I'd go home telling my husband who I'd seen that day: Marlon Brando, Gabriel Iglesias, Taye Diggs, Anderson Cooper. Of course, everywhere I looked, there was a little silver-haired Jessica Tandy.

I continued as a member of that medical exercise program for two years, working out three times a week. I felt so comfortable there that I imagined staying with the program for the rest of my life. Strengthening my body gave me a sense of mastery. Setting fitness goals took the place of other goals I'd formerly set for myself, goals that were no longer relevant or possible to reach.

But all good things come to end. In January 2017, I switched to a new health insurance plan that better served my needs. The new policy paid for a gym membership under the

Silver and Fit program. Sadly, the medical exercise clinic did not participate in this program. So, to take advantage of that benefit, I had to switch to a different gym.

I realized this change presented an opportunity to step up my game. At the new gym, I was no longer surrounded by physical therapists and their medically challenged clientele. Now, I found myself in the midst of musclebound, weight-lifting young men and very fit young women in stylish gym clothes. I suddenly felt the need to go shopping for better-looking workout gear.

After a rocky adjustment, during which I sorely regretted my decision to switch gyms, I have become quite comfortable in my new surroundings. Thankfully, the gym is dimly lit, which makes working out easier for me. I schedule my exercise times for the slow hours of the early afternoon so that I will not be overwhelmed by milling crowds.

In my new gym, I have pushed myself even harder, reaching higher levels of fitness. I thought perhaps my game of identifying celebrity look-alikes was over. However, when I spotted Bernie Sanders' body double among the *Silver and Fit* participants, I knew I could happily continue this nonsense.

Because I can now stride rapidly for more than thirty minutes on an elliptical or treadmill machine, it seems odd that I still have moments when my gait fails me. In such situations, it's as if a frail old woman appears out of nowhere, taking over my body for a time. But within minutes after I leave the troubling situation, she mysteriously disappears. My robust condition reasserts itself, and I resume my healthy gait.

My gratitude for my normally strong gait far outweighs the inconvenience of these setbacks. In terms of fitness, I am better off than I was during my years of sitting in an office. A silver lining of my limited ability to read and do close work, which are generally sedentary activities, is that I am now more inclined to be up and moving. Physical fitness is the one area in which the current me has an advantage over the pre-injury me.

I've come a long way from the day I lay unconscious in the middle of the road after being hit by a car.

This focus on fitness is probably prolonging my life. I am taking care of my health better than I ever have before. I sometimes ask myself, "Why am I strengthening my body, when a part of me longs to move on to the next phase of my soul's existence, a time when I will be free from physical and mental impairments? Is there something more for me to learn here on Planet Earth? Is there something more I need to offer? Am I strengthening myself for something that lies ahead?"

I don't know. I'm just curious.

A mantra that I often repeat in my mind is, *Guide my footsteps on this earth.* I hope that so long as I am here, my footsteps will be strong and purposeful.

Still, I sometimes wonder whether a time will come when my gait will completely fail me. Half a year after my surgery, I severely injured a toe and could barely walk for a few days. Two years after that, I sprained a wrist, which inhibited the use of my arm. Both times, I was afraid I would not recover. Would this injury be the one to leave me with a permanent impairment? Thankfully, neither one did. They presented only temporary obstacles to the full use of my limbs.

Since early childhood, I have been a vivid dreamer. Most of my dreams are nonsensical and deserve no attention. But some of them are important to me. They help me understand where I am on my emotional and spiritual journey. They speak to me from deep wisdom, giving me new perspectives on challenges in my life.

One of my favorite recurring dreams is about dancing. During the decade of my thirties, I was obsessed with dancing: folk dancing, contra dancing, ballroom dancing, square dancing, round dancing.

Now, I no longer dance, except for in my dreams. In my dance dreams, I am waltzing so lightly that my feet barely touch the ground. I always feel refreshed after such a dream.

In September 2015, nine months after my back surgery, I recorded an especially beautiful dance dream in my journal. A year later, I stumbled upon that journal entry while collecting notes for this book. I suddenly understood that if the day comes when my gait completely fails me, I will always have beautiful memories to draw upon. If the time comes when I am wheelchair bound, or even bedbound, I'll still be able to dance in my dreams.

MINDBLOWN

Several weeks after sustaining my brain injury, something terrifying happened to me. My husband had taken me to an appointment with the doctor who was coordinating my post-injury care. It was late in the afternoon, and I was tired. The glaring lights and the noise and commotion in the waiting room overwhelmed my senses. Once we were inside the doctor's office, my gregarious husband began shooting the bull with the doctor, and their lengthy conversation was one more thing I had to contend with. The appointment seemed to drag on forever.

On the way home, I had the sensation of my brain cells exploding out of my skull, whirling crazily in the air around me. I didn't understand what was happening to me. I desperately wanted to gather in all the deranged cells and settle them into place again. But I was powerless to do so.

Years later, I understand what happened that day. I was overstimulated by light, noise, commotion, and mental strain. My injured brain couldn't handle the stress, and went haywire. It had a meltdown.

Unfortunately, such experiences have become commonplace for me. I have small brain meltdowns on a daily basis. At times, this is characterized by a frantic feeling, a sensation of careening out of control. At other times, my brain feels dark, murky, and muddled. I often experience a sense of deep mental fatigue.

While the small episodes are painful, the major episodes are truly horrible. I think of them in terms of "hitting a wall." During such times, it feels as if all my nerves are screaming in agony. I can't get my bearings. I can't get a grip on a brain that is whirling in confusion. It feels as if I've lost my mind, as if I'm flying apart, all the pieces of me being scattered to the wind.

Sometimes, I can regroup from such an incident in an hour or two. More often, it takes a day or more to fully recover.

Prior to my injury, I worked a high-stress job in a community mental health center. I faced crises on a daily, sometimes hourly, basis. I had to bounce back quickly from each crisis, to regain my steady footing in a few seconds and move on to the next task that awaited me.

My injury has robbed me of the ability to be that resilient. What seems to be a normal, and even enjoyable, level of stimulation for most of the population doesn't line up with what I can tolerate. Ordinary stimulation often feels like unbearable bombardment to me. I sometimes think that if I lived my life at the level of stimulation and complexity of the average adult, my nervous system would be shredded to pieces. My fragility makes me feel like an oddity.

Sensory overload has become a big fear for me. Once, my husband said to me, "Since your injury, you've built a cocoon around yourself to keep from getting overstimulated."

Through seven years of post-injury experience, I've learned that some episodes of overstimulation can be avoided. If I plan my activities wisely, I can spare myself a great deal of pain. I know that if I pack too many household chores into a short period of time, I'll be frantic by the end of the day. I know that going to more than one social activity in a day is too much for me to handle. I've learned that spending an hour in a hair salon, with its noise, smells, and bright lights, is a painfully stimulating experience, and that if I choose to shop at the supermarket afterwards, I'm setting myself up for punishment.

When I have an exceptionally intense day, I feel so fragile that I hardly want anyone to look at me, let alone speak to me. It means that I'll need several quiet days to recover.

But I am far from perfect in applying the lessons that I've learned. Here is an example of a day when all my careful planning flew out the window. In the morning, I finished the final editing of one book and began the process of sorting notes for this book. Switching gears has been difficult for me since my injury, so moving from one project to another was stressful and disorienting.

Next, I attended a meeting with my book club. At times, the discussion became loud. At other times, several conversations were going on simultaneously. The auditory bombardment left me feeling dazed and exhausted.

That afternoon, I had a lunch meeting with a worker from Michigan Rehabilitation Services. The strain of our mentally taxing conversation was compounded by the noise and commotion in the restaurant. Immediately following that appointment, I had to drive to my eye clinic to meet with an optician, where we worked on solving problems associated with the glasses I was ordering.

I came home from this last appointment utterly exhausted, desperate to crawl back into my protective cocoon so that I could rest and regroup. But then, I received some news that sent my brain careening completely out of control.

It was wonderful news, but that didn't matter. Any news, good or bad, can throw me off balance. I received an email telling me that my novel, *A Weekend with Frances,* had been chosen to be featured in the *Kirkus Reviews* magazine as a "book of the month." At that moment, my world exploded into a million little pieces. That night, my brain was so overstimulated that the sleep I desperately needed to recover from my stressful day completely eluded me.

Obviously, some overstimulating events show up unexpectedly and cannot be warded off. One morning when I checked my email, a whole slew of messages popped up at one time. Something about that hit my brain the wrong way, throwing me into a weird mental space. It took me half a day to recover from that odd little incident.

After countless times of being startled by unexpected email messages, I have decided it is best to avoid checking my email in the evening. When I'm tired, a surprise message is too stimulating for me to handle. I inevitably find its contents to be overwhelming, even threatening, and I have difficulty relaxing and falling asleep. In the morning, when my brain is rested, I view that same email message in a different light, seeing it as innocuous or even containing something beneficial to me.

Sometimes, an unexpected phone call or something that arrives in the mail triggers a brain meltdown. In January 2017, I received a startling letter from my health insurance company, informing me that they were contacting my former auto insurance company to collect payment for my 2014 back surgery. They assumed that my herniated disc had resulted from me being hit by a car, and that my auto insurance was responsible for paying the associated medical expenses.

I immediately knew this was going to be a problem. My auto insurance had paid many claims in the aftermath of my accident, but my case with them had long been closed. Furthermore, my back surgery had nothing to do with the accident.

My mind zoomed to the possibility of a fight between the two insurance companies. I knew my former auto insurance would scoff at my health insurance's demand and would rightfully refuse to reimburse them for the surgery. I was certain that my health insurance would then turn to me, demanding that I reimburse the thousands of dollars they'd paid to the hospital and the surgeon.

This was a time when I didn't just hit the wall; the letter grabbed me by the hair and slammed me against the wall, knocking out any ability to think or make sense of the situation. It took me a week and many reassuring conversations with my husband to recover from that event.

In August 2016, my husband and I met with an insurance agent to talk about changing our auto and home policies. Despite the fact that I was wearing my wrap sunglasses, the intense fluorescent lighting in the agent's office got the better of me. He had given us papers to look at, which I couldn't read, and was talking rapidly, describing the benefits of the policy he was recommending to us.

I tried my best to follow what he was saying. But suddenly, something shut down in my brain, leaving me in a state of mental agony.

I told my husband that I needed to take a break, and that I was going to wait for him in the car. However, when I went outside, I realized that I didn't have a key to his vehicle. I stood there in the brutal heat and glaring sunlight, looking for a tree whose shade could provide me with relief from the sensory assault. There were none in sight.

By then, my gait had become slow and wobbly from the overstimulation. So, I hobbled back into the building and waited for Russ in the lobby, feeling mind-blown, confused, and miserable in every conceivable way.

On the way home, I was beside myself with exhaustion and agitation. "Am I getting worse?" I wailed to my husband. At that moment, I was afraid I was spiraling downward into full-blown dementia. But Russ assured me that I wasn't.

I feel so vulnerable during such episodes. It is hard to be alone at times like that. I always wish there was someone with me that I could rely on, someone who could put an arm around me and say, "It's okay. You'll feel better soon."

People who have known me only in my mentally intact state think I am just fine. If they've never witnessed me having such a meltdown, they might never suspect that I have a brain injury. Those who would see me only during such an episode might think that I have a severe disability. It's as if I am two different people. Even I can hardly recognize that these two states happen in the same person.

Given the enormous patience it takes to live with a brain-injured wife, the natural inclination would be for a spouse to snap on occasion, to berate his partner for her slowness, confusion, and fragility. While my husband has expressed anger over other matters in our relationship, I'm amazed that he's never lost his temper in response to my brain injury symptoms. After seven years of witnessing episodes of my brain meltdowns, Russ usually recognizes when things are starting to go wrong for me. Generally, he responds in a supportive manner.

But there have been a few occasions when my meltdowns have been misconstrued. One Saturday morning, as I was finishing the final round of editing a book, one particular task took my brain through a process it never had been through before. Indignant, my brain rebelled against the strain by crashing me headlong into the wall.

In a daze, I left my computer and stumbled downstairs to the kitchen, where I unwisely tried to help my husband with lunch preparations. He was not aware of my mental distress, and I was unable to effectively communicate to him what had happened. Interpreting my strange behavior as being ugly toward him, he got defensive. The tension between us only added to my distress.

When I finally succeeded in getting Russ to understand that I was having a bad brain moment, he said, "I'm trying not to be a jerk." He promptly left the house to cool down for a few minutes while I struggled to settle my deranged brain cells back into a semblance of order.

For several years after my injury, I attempted to involve myself with a spiritual study group held in Goshen, Indiana, where I formerly resided. Although I enjoyed the group immensely, I found it difficult to muster the energy to make the hour-long drive from my home to Goshen.

On several occasions, while focusing on tracking the stimulating group discussion, my brain suddenly let me know it had had enough. Something would shut down, leaving me in a state of distress and confusion. Once when this happened, I was in such mental agony that I had to immediately excuse myself and walk out of the meeting. "I'm not feeling well," I explained to the group members. I was very embarrassed.

The drive home after such meetings was always difficult, as I would be so exhausted. The next day, I would feel as if every cell in my brain had been pounded with a sledge hammer.

One lovely summer evening in 2016, I managed to make it all the way through the meeting without having a brain meltdown. We had gathered in the home of a man who owns a beautiful Dalmatian, a large dog who is nothing more than a puppy at heart. The dog was confined in another room during the meeting. I could hear her pitiful whimpers. She desperately wanted to come out and enjoy everyone's company.

After an hour of discussion, the group broke for refreshments. The milling of the crowd, along with the multiple high-energy conversations going on around me, began to overstimulate my brain. Then the dog's owner decided to let her out of her confinement. Exhilarated, she leaped and bounded around the room.

I love dogs, and I thought this Dalmatian was a splendid creature. I wanted to have a moment with her, to pet her and gush over her. But she wouldn't stand still for a second. As I tracked her movements, looking for an opportunity to reach out and pat her spotted head, her gyrations—the up and down and back and forth—suddenly overwhelmed my brain. It felt as if something exploded inside my skull. Dazed and confused, I stumbled out of the house to the safety of my car.

Deeply disappointed by this experience, I tried to figure out what I could do to prevent such episodes in the future. I decided that I needed to say goodbye to group members immediately after the discussion ended, declining to stay for refreshments, exiting the house before the Dalmatian was released from her confinement.

For five years after my injury, I attended a weekly writers group. The group met in the evening, at a time when my brain was tired from the day's activities and my reading capacity had been diminished.

The group process entailed each member reading his or her work aloud, while other members followed along on the printed copies that had been handed out. Each meeting, I would end up feeling sick from my efforts to read all that material. I always printed out my own work in a large font to make it easier for me to read. Still, when it came time for me to read aloud, I sometimes couldn't muster the eye power to do it and would ask for a surrogate reader. The lights in the room, coupled with the noisy discussions and the emotional tensions among group members, would add to my distress.

Every week, I left the group in a state of misery. I'd have difficulty falling asleep that night. The results of my overstimulation would last well into the next day. My husband repeatedly questioned whether attending the group was in my best interest.

But I continued to endure the pain because I wanted to learn everything I possibly could that would enhance my writing. Finally, in the summer of 2016, I reached a point of such misery that I forced myself to take stock of the situation. After thinking things through, I sadly recognized that the personal toll the meeting was taking on me now outweighed the benefits I was receiving. Grateful for everything I had learned, I made the decision to drop out of the group.

Any sensory stimulation can be overwhelming. One holiday season, as I walked through a display of scented candles in a department store, the fragrance assaulted my brain, sending me into a daze. My gait immediately failed me, and I moved slowly and shakily until I left the store.

On another occasion, I encountered a woman in the supermarket who was wearing a strong perfume. As she passed by me, a wave of exhaustion flowed through my brain, leaving me weak and dizzy for a few moments.

One winter day, when my husband and I went to pick up my car after it had been serviced, I found the noxious odors in the auto repair shop impossible to bear. While my husband dealt with the mechanic and paid the bill, I chose to avoid sensory overload by waiting outdoors in the inclement weather.

After a day of too much exposure to noise and chaos, I often have one of my commotion dreams. In this nightmare, hordes of people are streaming into my home uninvited. While they mill around, invading my personal space, I am screaming at them to get out of my house. But they refuse to do so. The only relief from the horror is to wake up from the dream.

When overstimulated, I often feel a desperate urge to crawl into a small, dark space that will protect me from further stimulation, so that I can gather back together all the parts of me that are flying apart. I wish I had access to one of the sensory deprivation chambers that were popular several decades ago. I am sure one of them would come in handy at the times of my greatest distress.

There are occasions, however, when I choose to break out of my protective cocoon to enjoy special events. In December 2016, my husband and I attended a performance of the *Messiah* at a local venue. The experience hammered my nervous system. To cut down on the sensory overload, I ended up listening to the concert with my eyes closed. It took me a day to recover from that event. But even though it took its toll on me, I counted it as worth the cost, as the memories of hearing that stunning performance have stayed with me ever since then.

After each episode of extreme overstimulation, my inner voice scolds me: *You must learn to take better care of yourself!* It is imperative that I learn from my experiences, as failure to use self-care skills can be so devastating.

Maintaining my stability has become a daily goal. On a good day, when I am peaceful and serene, I feel more centered than I've ever felt before. Still, I often feel a shadow of dread looming over me. I know that the serenity won't always be with me, that rough days and painful episodes of overstimulation will visit me again.

The only thing I can do is to take every possible measure to prevent the frequency of such episodes. I am still working on applying the basic lessons I've learned: to pace myself and not take on more than I can handle. To not push myself past the point where my brain tells me to stop. To pull back from an overstimulating situation before it gets the best of me. To let go of a task that is frustrating me, rather than trying to push through it. To recognize when it is time to shut down a project for the day and leave it for a time when I am in a better frame of mind.

I have come to understand that trying to solve a problem or complete a difficult task in a frantic state of mind never works. It only creates more problems. I have learned never to trust my judgment when I am in a state of overstimulation. At such times, my world looks hopeless and terrifying. A rested brain gives me a more accurate assessment of my situation.

Over the years, I have developed a toolkit of ways to get myself back on an even keel when I'm mind-blown. Early on, I discovered that rhythmic exercise is an excellent way to bring a frantic brain back into a state of tranquility. Thus, working out at the gym serves me well. Other remedies include lying down and listening to soft music with a warm pack over my tired eyes. Soaking in a tub of warm water in a darkened bathroom. Going for a walk in nature. Working in my flower gardens. Doing a household task that doesn't require much thought, such as folding laundry or putting away dishes.

When I am at a point of desperation, I resort to what I think of as my most extreme remedy: wading in the water along the shoreline of Lake Michigan. While this remedy is only available during the warm weather months, walking along the sandy beach works almost as well.

My Lake Michigan cure is a powerful one. At times, I have paced back and forth in the water for twenty or thirty minutes, allowing the deeply soothing effects of the lake to work its magic on my brain. Inevitably, I emerge from the water in a different state of mind.

I have always enjoyed working, as I like feeling productive. Recently, it has occurred to me that resting is actually productive. A brief nap can take me from feeling drained and ineffective to feeling renewed and ready to work again.

Not only does rest renew my body, it quiets my churning mind, allowing for inspiration and new ideas to enter. When I'm feeling exhausted and unable to cope with what I'm facing, I often say this prayer as I lie down for a nap: "I am preparing to rest. Please enter my mind and reshape my thoughts during this time."

A position I've learned in my Tai Chi class is "Stork Cools Its Wings." The left knee is slightly bent, the left arm remaining at the side. The right elbow is bent and the hand is raised. The position signifies the importance of stopping to rest after a period of intense activity.

This stork has learned that she needs to cool her wings. A lot.

POWER OUTAGES

My husband and I love living in Saint Joseph, a charming small town in southwestern Michigan. Not only do we enjoy the proximity to Lake Michigan, we appreciate the fact that Saint Joseph provides its residents with excellent services, beyond what you would expect from a city of our size. Russ and I can think of no better place to live.

However, for reasons unknown to me, the power goes out in Saint Joseph more frequently than anywhere else I have ever lived.

These power outages are sometimes associated with stormy weather, but not always. They do, however, seem to be highly correlated with times when I've stocked my freezer with ice cream.

We all know that if you want it to rain, the way to trigger an evening downpour is to spend the day watering your lawn. If you grow impatient while awaiting an important call, getting in the shower will make your phone ring. And if, for some perverse reason, you want the power to go out, then shopping for groceries and filling your refrigerator with perishables will cause it to happen.

One evening in January 2017, our power went out during a windstorm. My husband was at work. I sat alone in my dark house, unable to watch TV, use my computer, do laundry, or use the stove or microwave. I opted not to open the refrigerator, as I didn't want to increase the chances that our perishable food would spoil. I ended up going to bed early, lying there staring into the darkness.

The next morning, the power was still out, and my husband and I were unable to make coffee or fix breakfast. We had no hot water for showers. It had begun to grow very cold, as our house is heated by a boiler and the electric pump that circulates the water through our pipes was not working.

When the power finally came back on, I was overjoyed to have our usual conveniences available to us again. I remembered how grateful I am for the electricity that makes my life so much easier.

I suppose we could invest in a generator to avoid the inconveniences associated with such outages, but we have not yet decided to take on such an expense. All we can do is to wait until the electric company completes its job of restoring our power.

Unfortunately, since my brain injury, I experience episodes of power outage when it comes to certain mental functions. And there is no such thing as a generator to back up my brain when this happens. The only remedy for restoring power is time and rest.

For the past few years, Michigan Rehabilitation Services has worked with me on self-employment, helping me create a microbusiness of writing and selling my books. However, before we got to the point of determining what direction I would go with gainful employment, a few diagnostic steps had to be taken.

First, I had to have a neuropsychological evaluation, followed by an assessment of my functioning within my home. Then I was sent to a nearby town for a four-day employment evaluation.

The agency that conducted my employment evaluation primarily serves developmentally disabled adults, helping them secure and maintain employment commensurate with their skill levels. Walking into that agency as a client was a profoundly humbling experience for me. Over the course of my career, I had provided services to many developmentally disabled individuals. Now, I was no longer the professional. I was numbered among the disabled, one of the clientele. Sitting in the waiting room, I was overwhelmed with grief.

There were only two other people in the room with me during my evaluation: the person conducting the assessment and a developmentally disabled young man who was also undergoing the evaluation.

The bulk of the assessment consisted of pencil and paper tests. Throughout all the years of my education, from elementary through graduate school, I had been a good test-taker. My ability to sail through an exam had helped to keep my GPA high. In addition to ordinary classroom exams, I'd performed well on lengthy tests such as the SAT, the ACT, and the National Merit Scholarship qualifying test.

The first test of the employment evaluation covered basic academic skills. I completed it with confidence and answered 100% of the questions correctly. But then something happened. On subsequent tests, I began to sputter and fail. My brain would reach a point on the exam where it would shut down. I'd stare at a question, unable to comprehend the meaning of it, unable to move forward. And because I was able to complete only a small portion of the questions in the time allotted for each test, I ended up scoring very low on most of the exams.

On days two, three, and four of the evaluation, I was exhausted before I even sat down to take my first test. Again, my brain shut down after a few questions, and I continued to score poorly.

This experience hit me hard. There was no denying the fact that my brain injury had impacted my cognitive abilities. I had retained most of my old abilities, but they were available to me only part of the time. Exhaustion had the power to sweep them right out of my brain. I was no longer the skilled test-taker I once had been. I had lost a piece of myself.

When my brain begins to tire, the power growing dim, I have difficulty organizing concepts I want to express. I am unable to line up thoughts the way I want to. When I write, I often feel as if I am working in a fog, not comprehending what I have written or what I am trying to say. I am often amazed that I am able produce anything coherent.

But when I am exhausted, I have more problems with numbers than I do with words. Despite the fact that I long ago forgot how to do higher levels of math, such as trigonometry, I'd always retained my competence in basic math. I can still do math just fine—but only when my brain power is on full blast. The minute the power grows dim, my ability to work with numbers flies out the window. I have difficulty balancing a checkbook or understanding the numbers in my online bank account. If I try to struggle through the difficulty on my own, the problem worsens. I frequently need to ask my husband to check my work.

My ability to handle money also fails me when my brain power begins to falter. This puts me at a disadvantage when selling books at a public event. I can make change when someone hands me money for the first book. But after that, confusion sets in, and I lose track of what I am doing.

In December 2016, I was offered the opportunity to sell my books at an art fair at a local library. The event took place on a Friday evening, when my husband was at work. I wanted to take advantage of the opportunity, but was terrified that the highly stimulating environment would exhaust me and lead to a shutdown of my cognitive abilities. How would I manage to handle financial transactions if such a thing happened?

In desperation, I reached out to a friend from my church, telling her about my dilemma. She graciously responded by arranging for three different church members to sit with me at the fair in shifts.

As it ended up being a cold, snowy night, there wasn't much traffic through the art fair. Still, being cared for by my friends made it a gratifying experience.

When my brain power grows dim, I am unable to understand what others are trying to explain to me. Many times, I remain silent, letting the moment pass without revealing my mental struggle. Thus, most people never have a clue that I have cognitive problems.

Occasionally, I need to mail a book or manuscript, which requires a trip to the post office. Managing the transaction at the post office window defeats me every time. I always want to know the least expensive way to mail my package, but I rarely understand what the fast-speaking postal clerk is trying to tell me. After a great deal of fumbling, I exit the post office exhausted and humiliated. I'm sure my lack of understanding has resulted in me spending more money on shipping than I've needed to.

One day in September 2017, I was faced with the daunting task of mailing four books to a customer. This time, I asked my husband to come with me, as I feared I would not be able to manage on my own. After consulting with the postal clerk, Russ assisted me in selecting the shipping envelope that best suited my needs. As my hands had become weak and clumsy by then, he inserted the books into the envelope for me. Using every ounce of my diminishing concentration, I filled out the address label. My husband stood there whistling as he waited on me. I had to ask him to stop, as the distracting sound was impeding my ability to focus on my writing.

"I can see why you didn't want to come alone," he commented as we left the post office.

In December 2016, I saw an ad on TV inviting Medicare participants to call an 800 number to learn about benefits for which they might be eligible. I had been wanting to enroll in a plan that included vision and dental benefits. On impulse, I called the 800 number to learn more about that possibility.

I ended up talking with one person after another, all who spoke rapidly while explaining available plan options. I could not comprehend a thing any of them said to me.

Before I knew it, I was being asked to give my verbal consent to sign up for a plan. Bewildered, I went along with the process, even though I had no idea what I was doing. After I hung up the phone, I was terrified.

"Why didn't you talk with me about this first?" my husband scolded after I told him what I'd done. We were both afraid I had inadvertently signed up for something that would create problems for me.

So, the next day, I called the insurance agent to whom I'd given my verbal consent. This time, I informed the gentlemen that I had a brain injury, and that it took me longer to comprehend what was being explained to me. I asked him to slowly take me through the features of the plan I'd signed up for. He assured me that if I didn't want the plan, I could discontinue it at any time.

After the agent's patient explanation, I realized that what I had blindly stumbled into would actually be a good thing for me. Days later, I received a packet of information in the mail, which my husband went over with me. Not only did I receive the vision and dental benefits I'd wanted, the plan paid for the gym membership I have since enjoyed. I finally felt confident in moving forward with my new plan.

I learned a valuable lesson from this experience. When someone is explaining something critical to me, I need to ask them to slow down. It is imperative that I ask questions until I am fully confident that I understand clearly.

On a beautiful spring day in 2017, I had one of my most frightening experiences with a cognitive power outage. In the morning, I tried to cram in too many household tasks before leaving for Tai Chi, which rendered me tired before class even started. But I threw myself into the class, savoring the experience. The hour was lovely, even though my brain was exhausted by the time it was over.

I usually go straight home after my class. But that day, I needed to drive to a health food store in downtown Saint Joseph to pick up vitamins.

Finding a parking space downtown is often a tricky matter. As I circled around several blocks trying to find a spot near the store, I felt the power in my tired brain growing dimmer and dimmer. I finally succeeded in parking, bought my vitamins, and then drove home.

When I pulled into my garage, I suddenly couldn't remember how to get out of my car. My brain power was so depleted that I couldn't spot the door handle. This cognitive lapse terrified me. For a few minutes, I sat there trapped, not knowing what to do. I almost resorted to pulling out my cell phone and calling my husband, who was in the house, to come out and help me. Thankfully, I didn't need to do this, as I finally found the handle.

After taking a break for lunch, I went outdoors to weed a flowerbed. I hoped this relaxing activity would get me back on an even keel and recharge my brain. But even though I was outside for no more than thirty minutes, the intensity of the April sunlight was too stimulating for me. When I went inside, I felt dizzy and lightheaded.

Unwisely, I went upstairs to my computer to pay several bills online. In the middle of that process, I became so confused that I couldn't make sense of what I was doing. The numbers I was trying to work with became a jumble, and I couldn't comprehend why the balance in my bank account was what it was.

The incident shook me so badly that I decided I should no longer attempt to pay bills without my husband's help. However, when I awoke the next morning, my confusion was gone. Cognitively, I felt much better. I managed to pay our mortgage bill, although by the end of the process I began to feel the first flickers of diminishing brain power.

One cognitive function that has been affected by my injury is my ability to sort, especially when my brain is tired. I suspect this difficulty is a combination of cognitive and visual functions. Sorting through important paperwork is daunting and mentally painful. Sorting through notes for this book has been a torturous process.

Even sorting laundry becomes difficult when I am tired. In my basement laundry room, I have a row of baskets into which I put laundry for different loads. If my mental power is spent, things are bound to end up in the wrong basket. The same holds true if I try to put laundry away in drawers and closets when I am exhausted.

One evening at my writers group, the attendance was unusually large. I hadn't brought enough copies of my work for everyone there, so I resorted to making additional copies on the group's copier. I then had to do some collating.

Unfortunately, the sorting function in my brain completely shut down. I ended up on my knees on the floor with a jumble of papers spread out in front of me, incapable of putting the pages in the right order. My inability to complete my task humiliated me. Finally, the group leader asked another member to help me with the collating project. My brain was screaming in agony by the time I was finished with the task.

At home, I've come up with a technique for my problem with sorting. I pile everything that needs to be sorted into one spot, such as the dining room table. Having everything in one location allows me to chip away at the task a little bit at a time.

Between episodes, I tend to have a bit of amnesia about these power outages. When my brain is clicking along just fine, I convince myself that my cognitive challenges are a thing of the past. Then, when another outage hits, I am sadly reminded that the problem is still with me.

That day in January 2017, when the power came back on after being out for thirteen hours, I was so grateful for the convenience of electricity. I made coffee and fixed breakfast, enjoying the food in my refrigerator that, happily, hadn't spoiled. Then I carried on with my normal daily activities: using my computer, doing laundry, and running the vacuum cleaner.

In the same vein, I am so thankful when, after I've rested and recharged, the power comes back on in my brain. I am grateful for every moment that I can think clearly, every moment that I can do math, balance my checkbook, sort through paperwork, sort laundry, or make sense of a writing project. I know that I am fortunate to have retained most of my brain power at least part of the time.

LIST OF LISTS

I am a neat freak. I won't deny that I'm a little obnoxious in my insistence on order. I like everything around me to be clean and tidy. I like my daily activities to be well-organized and to flow smoothly. My free-spirited husband thinks this is a sign of obsessive-compulsive disorder. Clinically, I don't qualify for that diagnosis, but I admit that I do have tendencies in that direction.

I know exactly where my neat-freak gene came from. When I was a child, my parents had difficulty keeping our overcrowded house tidy and well-organized. On the rare occasions when we visited my paternal grandparents, I'd catch a glimpse of a different lifestyle. My tiny German grandmother, in her long dark dresses and Mennonite head-covering, ended up in a wheelchair in her last years. But her infirmity didn't stop her. She'd wheel around her mobile home dusting shelves and table tops. Never did I see a speck of dirt in her house, or a cobweb in some overlooked corner. Never did I see clutter. Embarrassed about the conditions in my own home, I'd say to myself, "This is the way things should be done."

Much to my consternation, I was diagnosed with an "attention problem" in the aftermath of my brain injury. That is a very untidy disorder, a messy mental process. Said my brilliant daughter who struggles with attention deficit disorder, "Now you know what I have to deal with, Mom. Since your accident, you've become like me."

When my brain is well-rested, I am still able to organize the big picture. I can plan what I want to do today, tomorrow, and next week. I am able to formulate a project, listing the steps I need to take to get to my desired outcome. In a controlled environment, where I am alone in a quiet room with pencil and paper in hand, the organizing process moves along just fine.

But while I can plan the big picture, concentration is a problem for me. My difficulty comes when I am trying to focus on the tasks I set out to do. When the unpredictability of daily life starts happening, when normal pressures start impinging upon me, my brain spins in confusion. I easily lose track of what I'm doing. Many times, I've come across a household task that I started, then got distracted and failed to complete.

Multitasking is difficult for me. When I am pulled in too many directions, numerous things simultaneously calling for my attention, my brain is in pain. Shifting gears multiple times in rapid succession exhausts me, rendering me weak and confused. I can feel my brain power faltering, fighting to stay on.

I struggle with a type of memory problem that makes it difficult to keep a thought in my mind. I might have an idea for a writing project, a household task I want to do, or something important that I need to tell my husband. But in a split second, the thought is gone, swallowed up by a black hole in my brain, not a trace of it left behind. I will remember that I had an important thought, but the content of that thought will be unavailable to me.

The thought might reappear an hour later, or even days later. I'll think, "I was going to do that. I'll do it now." If I'm lucky, I will retain the idea long enough the second time to get the job done. If I don't, the thought might keep circling around, coming back to me again and again before I successfully act on it.

This process of setting an intention, struggling to hold it in my brain, and then losing focus is mentally exhausting. If I try to hold onto several intentions at the same time, my brain becomes so tired that I can hardly function.

I not only forget what I intend to do, I also forget what I've just done. Did I take my vitamins? Did I put a fabric softener sheet in the dryer? Did I brush my teeth? I frequently resort to checking my toothbrush to see if it is still wet.

Especially when I'm tired, I have difficulty retaining information that has just been presented to me. During my years of attending the writers group, people would often read aloud a poem or a passage of prose. If I had no paper copy in front of me for reference, the beginning and middle of the piece would have fled my mind by the time the reader reached the end. Thus, I'd be unable to participate in the discussion that followed.

Most of the time, I can remember details such as my social security number, my address, and my phone number. However, there are occasions when something happens in my brain that prevents me from accessing that familiar information. One day when I received some upsetting news, I went into a panic. My husband was at work, and I wanted to call him immediately.

I'd previously called Russ's cell phone hundreds of times. But that day, I encountered a barrier in my brain that blocked access to the memory of his number. I could actually see the obstacle in my mind's eye. It looked like a white curtain. No matter how hard I tried, I could not get around that curtain to find the information I needed.

I knew his number would be on my cell phone. So, instead of calling Russ from our landline phone as I usually do, I pulled out my rarely-used cell phone and called him from that.

The following day, I could easily remember my husband's phone number again.

My two oldest children both have birthdays in July. One day, when I was thinking about the fact that my daughter Chantelle's birthday was coming up, I couldn't remember whether it was July 27 or 29. I wracked my brain, but was unable to access that information. I was just about to pull out the baby book I'd kept on her, as I knew her birthdate would be recorded there. Then I remembered that her birthday was twelve days after my son Zane's birthday, which is on the 17th.

Since then, I've never forgotten that Chantelle's birthday is July 29. Hopefully, my brain has permanently recovered that piece of information. But these gaps in memory are terrifying.

When I first realized that this messy-brained condition was the new state of affairs in my life, I was appalled and humiliated. "This is unacceptable," I said to myself. "I am not going to function like this." So, I set about finding ways to compensate for my attention and memory challenges.

The structure I've created to shore up my struggling brain is one of the things I am most proud of accomplishing in the aftermath of my injury. This structure has allowed me to emerge from that disabling event appearing relatively intact. It is one reason why many people do not recognize the fact that I have a brain injury.

Throughout my years of working in a fast-paced career, my

primary organizational aid was my never-ending "to do" list. At the close of each work day, I'd create a list of things I wanted to accomplish the following day. Unpredictable events constantly modified my list throughout the day. Continually jotting down new tasks I needed to address freed up mental space and kept me moving forward.

To an extent, I had used "to do" lists in my home life, also. But after my injury, when confusion hampered my effectiveness in getting things done, I realized I needed to rely more heavily on lists. And that is what I have done over the past seven years.

Now, I keep several neat stacks of lists on my dresser top, next to a calendar. They serve as my guides throughout the day. Most important is my basic list of activities for the day, which I've created on my computer. Some of the activities are the same for every day, ranging from making my bed to flossing my teeth to taking my vitamins. Additionally, there are lines for writing in appointments and activities specific for a certain day.

Other lists in my dresser-top stacks pertain to exercising, cleaning the house, and maintaining my flower gardens. And a few more lists get posted on the refrigerator.

Most people would feel confined by operating from lists to the extent that I do. My husband is one of them. He keeps ideas and intentions in his head. He teases me, telling me that my lists are proliferating to the extent that I might someday need to make a list of all my lists. He would not be surprised if this happened.

But the lists work for me, and I don't feel inclined to get rid of them. They serve as compasses that point me in the right direction when I wander off course. When I've become overstimulated and confused, my lists help me find my bearings again. After cognitive power outages, looking at a list helps to reorient me to the here and now and get me back on track. If I am too mind-blown to address the task in front of me, logging it on a list eases my mind. I know that I will be prompted to take care of the matter when I am mentally able to do so.

Without my lists, I'd spend my days spinning in confusion, struggling to find a forward momentum. My lists help me get more done in a shorter timeframe. They help me function like a "normal" person.

To compensate for my problems with vision, concentration,

multitasking, fatigue, and episodes of slow gait and clumsy hands, I have come up with ways of doing chores in a more efficient manner, developing some deeply ingrained habits. I have discovered that using the right tool, the right technique, the right routine, and the right arrangement increases my efficiency and decreases my frustration. Thus, I am able to take care of my home and property better than I did prior to my injury.

For a while, I found watering houseplants to be a frustrating task, as I would tend to forget where I was in the project. So, I developed a routine that helped me complete the task in a timely manner. However, one October, I brought in a number of potted plants I'd kept outdoors, intending to store them in the house during the cold weather months. Accommodating the new plants involved rearranging the plants I already had in the house.

The first time I attempted to water plants after this change, I struggled in confusion. My routine had been altered. I couldn't remember which plants I'd watered, and which ones still needed watering. It took far too long to get the task done. I had to develop a new routine before I could complete the watering chore with ease.

I've also developed habits to help compensate for my memory problem. If I have a thought I want to remember when I'm away from home, I write a note to myself, then put it in the compartment of my handbag where I keep my car keys. When I get home and put my keys away, I always see the note.

When I need to hold a thought or intention in my mind for a minute or two, I often repeat it aloud, over and over like a broken record, until I can get to the place where I can act on it. I frequently forget where I've stored something. To prevent this, while putting something away, I say aloud several times, "I'm putting (this object) right here in this (drawer, cupboard, closet)." To keep myself from forgetting what I've just done, I sometimes repeat aloud what I am doing: "I am taking my vitamins." Or, "I am putting detergent in the washing machine."

In terms of multitasking, mornings are particularly difficult for me. My husband works the second shift, leaving for his job around noon. Thus, mornings are the time when we take care of matters pertaining to household business. I have questions to ask him, or tasks with which I need his help. Additionally, I have my usual list of morning chores. All of this results in many rapid shifts in focus for me. As the morning hours pass, I feel increasingly frantic and confused. By 11:00 AM, I'm often in sorry shape, dazed and exhausted, unable to think straight.

I began to dread my morning routine, knowing that it would inevitably cause me distress. Then I realized what I needed to do. I made my list of morning activities more detailed than it had been before. I added tasks I'd previously thought I could do automatically. Although mornings are still difficult, amending my list has helped a great deal. I don't have to struggle so much with trying to hold thoughts and intentions in my brain.

One chore I used to have difficulty with was cleaning the bathroom. Inevitably, I'd find myself getting distracted during the process by something else that was calling for my attention. Then I'd forget where I was in the cleaning process, and would become anxious about whether I was remembering to do everything that needed to be done.

I finally resorted to making a list of the steps involved with cleaning the bathroom, which has helped me tremendously. After completing each step, I mark it off the list. That way, if I need to walk away for some reason, I know exactly what is done and what steps are needed to finish the job.

Prior to making this bathroom-cleaning list, addressing that chore had seemed overwhelming to me. Taking it one step at a time makes the task entirely manageable.

Writing my most recent novel, *Hope's New Season,* was, for the most part, a joyful and entertaining project. But in December 2016, when I came to the end of the story, I was faced with the tedious and unsatisfying task of formatting the book. Formatting and editing functions generally mean weeks of me being upset and emotionally out of kilter.

"I just dread this phase of my writing," I told my husband. "My brain hates it."

When I found myself becoming increasingly depressed over the prospect of taking on the formatting project, I knew I had to do something to lessen the pain. I didn't want to repeat the miserable experience I'd had with previous books. So, I wrote down the steps it would take to complete the project. As I completed each step and marked it off my list, I enjoyed a sense of accomplishment.

Sometimes, Russ takes over a portion of a complex task, sparing me a great deal of brain strain. While reading the proof copy of *Hope's New Season,* I marked the errors, simultaneously compiling a list of the pages on which corrections were needed. Then, I had to turn to making the corrections in the computer manuscript. I knew this would entail a long, visually strenuous process of going back and forth between the book, the list, and the computer screen, a multitasking effort that would drive me out of my mind.

Thankfully, my husband was available to help. He sat beside me while I sat at my keyboard. While I kept my eyes on the computer screen, he held the list and the proof copy of the book, giving me verbal instructions regarding where each correction needed to be made. We accomplished the task relatively easily, saving me from an agonizing brain meltdown.

Cooking is a multitasking venture that remains difficult for me. Sometimes, even the thought of making a salad for lunch—washing and cutting up vegetables—overwhelms me. I never do well with meals for special occasions, even though my husband does much of the work.

On Thanksgiving Day 2016, Russ and I worked all day preparing food before sharing an evening meal with my children. As it was a dark, overcast day, I spent far too much time under artificial lighting. By the end of the day, I was suffering from a throbbing headache. Cognitively, I was barely hanging on, trying my best to function in a state of confusion.

The next morning, I woke up feeling terrible. As I tried to muster the energy to get myself going, I stared out my bedroom window at the creatures enjoying the holiday feast Russ had spread out for them on our backyard patio.

"Maybe we should do like the birds and squirrels next Thanksgiving," I told my husband. "Nibble on an ear of corn or peck at a few seeds."

I spent that day in deep thought, contemplating the events of the previous day, knowing that I never wanted to repeat such a scenario. I knew, without a doubt, that my top priority on holidays was spending time with my children. But our shared meal had to change. It was time to give up the idea of serving a traditional dinner on an elegantly set table.

So, a month later at Christmastime, Russ and I served a simple buffet-style meal. On other special occasions, we have opted to take my children out to eat.

Clutter creates confusion for me. The sight of a mess can derail my thoughts. When I was preparing to write the first chapters of this book, I used my dining room table as a place to spread out dozens of notes on small scraps of paper. The notes lay on the table for the better part of a week, while I tried in vain to sort them and arrange them in the right order. I couldn't stand the sight of the mess, and felt unsettled every time I passed by it. I had to devise another method of handling my notes, one that kept them tucked out of sight.

To prevent a mess from building up around me, I work hard at keeping clutter out of my house. I periodically go through a drawer, a cupboard, or a closet to remove items Russ and I no longer use, donating them, recycling them, or throwing them away. Periodically, I enlist my husband's help in sorting through old, unneeded documents. If I allowed clutter to overtake my life, I'd end up in a chronic state of agitation and confusion.

I know from painful experience that if I take on a project in the house or yard that creates too much disorder in my space, it sends me into a very dark mental place. I've learned to tackle such projects in smaller, less disruptive steps.

My "head-writing" is a messy ordeal, with inspiration coming at inopportune times and places. It clutters my brain, and could easily clutter my living space. My two-basket solution helps to tidy up this disorderly process.

Prior to implementing my basket routine, I was simply placing head-writing notes on a stairstep. The right side of the staircase was for my notes. The left side was for my husband's things, such as mail and receipts that he wanted to take to his upstairs office. Sometimes, I'd leave a note on his side of the stairs, reminding him of something I needed him to do.

One day, I inadvertently put a head-writing note on Russ's side of the stairs. He picked it up, thinking it was a note I'd written to him. Bewildered, he read a piece of dialog intended for my novel, *Blessed Transgression*. It was a scene in which Victoria, a teenage girl, was getting herself ready for a meeting with the birth father she despised. I had scribbled her thoughts on a scrap of paper: *Why are you doing this? You might as well go looking like a slob. You don't care what that jerk thinks about you.*

Russ initially assumed I was trying to send him a rude message. When he figured out that it was one of my head-writing notes, we both laughed at the mistake I'd made.

I keep a cash box for events at which I sell books. I've always tried to have plenty of small bills on hand, so that I can make change when I need to. If my brain is even a little bit tired, counting money and making change is difficult for me.

After an embarrassing incident in which I struggled to provide a customer with change, I had an epiphany. I realized that too many bills in my cash box had turned into clutter, and that the clutter had impeded my thought processes when I was trying to figure out what change I needed to hand to the customer. So, I cleared out the excessive bills and whisked them off to the bank, resolving to keep fewer bills in the box.

As with visual clutter, I am unable to think straight when there are multiple sources of auditory stimulation in my environment. So, as much as possible, I keep my environment quiet. I never have the television or music playing when I am trying to concentrate.

I've learned that I function best when I move slowly, deliberately, and mindfully through my daily activities, focusing on only one thing at a time. Rushing throws me off balance. I do best with predictability and routine.

Others might find my lifestyle stifling and insufferably boring. Sometimes, it becomes that way for me, too. Whenever my life feels as if it has been reduced to vacuuming floors, doing laundry, and weeding flowerbeds, I know it is time to step out of my routine to become a spontaneous and free-spirited human being.

So, I have days when I shake things up and do something I

ordinarily don't do. I go on an outing, arrange something differently in my house, plant something new in my flowerbeds, eat something different, wear something different—anything to give me a fresh perspective on life. When the day is over, I am inevitably exhausted by the change in pace, and am eager to return to the comfort of the routines that work so well for me.

In April 2017, I watched a TV show about interior designers who were preparing a home for a woman who'd suffered a traumatic brain injury. They were focusing on eliminating unnecessary sensory stimulation, in order to create a "sanctuary" and a "healing space" for the injured woman. Clearly, the designers believed the woman deserved those special accommodations. She was profoundly grateful for what they did for her.

As I watched their work, I realized I'd never believed that I deserved my own healing space. I've always had difficulty seeing myself as deserving of anything. Instead, I have tended to push myself in an effort to prove that I am a worthwhile human being.

Countless times since my injury, I have pushed myself harder than what my brain could handle. Instead of focusing on fostering a healing environment, I have criticized myself for not being normal, for not doing better, for not accomplishing more. I have lived in fear of the judgements of others, internalizing the comments and expectations of people who don't understand brain injuries.

The wisest part of me has finally decided it is imperative that I create a healing space in my home, to maximize the amount of time that I am able to stay calm, serene, and functioning at my best. That is beneficial, not only for me, but for everyone around me.

I know I'll tend to fall back into old patterns of pushing myself too hard. But I have promised myself that each time I do that, I will renew my commitment to maintaining my personal healing environment.

LIKE A LITTLE CHILD

Although traumatic brain injury never was my specialty during my career, I did have a handful of brain-injured clients throughout the years I worked as a psychotherapist. I was exposed to enough of their problems to understand some of the challenges the brain-injured population faces.

One thing that struck me about these clients was that their emotions seemed childlike, at odds with their status of mature adulthood.

The first brain-injured client I ever saw was a middle-aged woman who had sustained head trauma when she fell off a ladder. Since then, she had not been employed. Her elderly mother-in-law suffered from dementia, and the family was struggling to arrange appropriate care for her. Because my client wasn't working, family members assumed that she'd be an optimal candidate to look after her ailing relative.

My client came to see me because of her inability to cope with the task of caring for her mother-in-law. She believed that she should be able to do the job, but found that she just couldn't manage it. She was frustrated with herself, and was afraid her family was upset with her.

As uninformed as I was about brain injury at the time, I quickly saw what the problem was. My client was physically and cognitively capable of providing care for someone with dementia, but was emotionally unable to bear up under the stress. I suspected her family didn't understand that fact.

Another of my clients had sustained a brain injury in an auto accident. She had recovered enough to hold down a part-time job. But she had difficulty controlling her impulses and her anger. She was an attractive young woman who had no problem finding a boyfriend. However, she was unable to maintain a long-term relationship because she couldn't stop herself from verbally abusing her partners. I once witnessed her exploding at her boyfriend in the waiting room when he said something innocuous that struck her wrong.

A third client also sustained a brain injury in an auto accident. She was an intellectually gifted woman who had formerly worked in a professional capacity. As she was now unemployed, her parents assumed she was available to shoulder a difficult family problem. They put her in charge of overseeing the renovation of one of their properties that had been damaged in a fire.

"I just can't do it," my client tearfully confessed to me. The stress associated with addressing this complex task completely overwhelmed her. She felt like a failure, and I felt profoundly sorry for her.

Once, my supervisor observed this client standing at the reception desk in the waiting room with tears running down her face. "She was crying like a little child," he told me.

Years later, I am no longer the therapist who dispenses empathy from her lofty perch. I now see these childlike emotions in myself. I am well aware of the fact that I've humiliated myself by becoming emotionally overwrought in public places.

A year after my injury, I sat weeping in a doctor's office over problems with my insurance. Another day, I behaved in an agitated manner in the Social Security office. Over the telephone, I railed at the supervisor of a medical provider I believed had done me wrong. I'm sure that when the supervisor hung up the phone, he thought he'd just talked to a crazy person. I drafted a nasty "letter to the editor" regarding this same medical provider, but my husband wisely discouraged me from sending it to our local newspaper.

Early on, my husband started reminding me to "be nice" before I made difficult phone calls regarding personal business. Now, years after my injury, I remind myself to be nice. I am, in fact, mindful of being gracious to the people who serve me, trying to make up for my earlier bratty behavior.

I am not proud of my emotional fragility, but I must accept that it is now a part of me. Since my injury, I seem to have lost a defense mechanism that protects me from overwhelming emotions. It seems as if some moderating device is no longer in play, as when strong emotions hit, they hit hard. And it takes me a long time to settle down after becoming overwrought.

Being this fragile is painful and humiliating. I have, at times, been scolded for my strong emotions, which has made me feel ashamed of myself.

In November 2012, I turned sixty. This was the most traumatic milestone birthday I'd ever experienced. In my mind, the event marked the transition from middle-age to my senior years. Intense, crazy emotions churned inside me. On top of all that, I felt let down when my husband didn't do what I thought he should have done to mark the occasion.

After letting Russ know in no uncertain terms that he hadn't done right by me, I spent a sleepless, emotionally distraught night. Around five o'clock in the morning, when it was still dark outside, I left the house and walked the quarter of a mile to Lake Michigan, where I paced up and down the sandy shore in a state of agitation. Thankfully, I was able to calm myself enough to return home in a more reasonable frame of mind. I encountered no one on my weird adventure except for a solitary man walking his dog.

The most significant event that marked the passage into my sixtieth year took place in a dream. Evidently to quiet my unrelenting tantrum, an unknown being walked into my bedroom and placed a vase containing three white roses on my bedside stand. Then he was gone.

After calming down from my stormy lakeside visit, I told my husband about the dream. Not wanting to be outdone by the nighttime apparition, he promptly went out and bought three white roses, which he placed on my bedside stand.

Sometime after my birthday, I wrote a letter to my friend Roseanne, telling her about my walk to the lake in the early morning darkness. In her return letter, she gave me a well-deserved scolding. "Lois," she said, "that was dangerous. Please promise me you'll never do that again."

I suddenly realized how foolishly I'd acted, and felt embarrassed. I readily promised Roseanne that I'd never repeat such silly behavior.

My father died in 2004 and my mother in 2009, both passing before I sustained my brain injury in 2010. From my professional training, I'd known about the elements and stages of grief. During my parents' final illnesses and at their deaths, I experienced what I thought to be normal grief processes.

But when my older brother died in 2013, two and a half

years after my injury, my grieving was altogether different. I couldn't recognize the craziness in my brain. "What the heck is going on with me?" I asked myself time and again.

My brother had lived in Arizona. Thus, news regarding the status of his health in his final months came from a distance, from several different sources. Often, these sources gave conflicting reports, one suggesting that he was recovering while others indicated that his condition was rapidly declining. So, I had difficulty knowing what was actually going on.

My confusion agitated me, even enraged me. After each episode of hearing conflicting news, I would rant in frustration. My sorrow over my brother's illness turned into something that felt like insanity.

During this time, I wrote rambling letters to my friend Roseanne, filled with unfiltered emotion. I later wondered how crazy I must have sounded to her.

After my brother passed, I realized that my brain injury had altered my ability to manage grief. I knew that I'd inevitably need to face grief over the passing of other family members, and that terrified me. For years, whenever the phone rang, I was afraid it was someone calling with the news of another death in the family. I wasn't sure I could handle the intensity of my emotions a second time.

In the summer of 2016, our nation—and the entire world—was shaken by a series of shootings and terrorist attacks. I was attending my medical exercise program at the time, and I often watched the news on television while I did my cardio workout.

One day in July, I watched the coverage of a shooting in Dallas, Texas. Turning to my friend Gloria, who was exercising nearby, I said, "It seems like every time we turn on the TV, we see news about another shooting. I wonder where the next one will be."

To my utter disbelief, the next shooting reported on national news was one that took place in my tiny town of Saint Joseph, Michigan. When I heard about the horrific incident, my thoughts and emotions careened out of control. I couldn't grasp the fact that such a shooting took place a mile from my home. It felt as if there was no safety anywhere.

This was not a terrorist-related shooting. It happened in the county courthouse. An inmate from the jail was being escorted to the courtroom by a bailiff. The prisoner suddenly turned on the bailiff and wrestled his gun away, killing him and a second bailiff.

The tragic event left the community in a state of shock. Business at the courthouse was shut down for several days. When Russ and I drove past the empty building, we could sense the pall of grief hanging over it.

The day after the shooting, I sent frantic emails to friends and family members, informing them of the news. I called my friend Roseanne in a state of agitation. She did her best to calm me down.

Several days after the incident, a memorial walk was scheduled for the victims of the shooting. I wanted to be a good citizen and participate in the event. But I knew I'd never be able to stand up to the sweltering heat and blazing sunlight of the July day.

So, I turned to the idea of attending a vigil scheduled to be held downtown that evening. I wanted very much to lend my support to the community in its grief. My husband was at work at his second-shift job, so I knew I'd have to venture out on my own.

Several hours before the vigil, I made a trial run to the location where it was to be held. But it was tourist season, and I couldn't find any place to park downtown. I knew that a parking spot would be even harder to find later that evening. As I drove around town, I started feeling dazed and confused, and I knew I'd be even worse off several hours later. I finally had to admit to myself that attending the event was not an option for me.

That evening, while people in the community gathered a mile away, I held my vigil at home. Tearfully and prayerfully, I joined with the mourners in their grief and their desire for peace in our community and in the world.

I had wanted to be a normal citizen, to do what others are able to do in such a situation. But after struggling and failing to find a way to participate in this community event, I realized once again that my lifestyle needs to be a modified one. I do what I can, which isn't everything most people are capable of doing.

I also realized that, to keep from drowning in an ocean of overwhelming sorrow, I had to put an emotional shield between myself and such happenings. For days after the hate-crime shootings in the church in Charleston and the terrorist activity in the Orlando nightclub, I cried every time thoughts of the events entered my mind. After the shooting in my own community, I became so distraught and disoriented that I ended up being a detriment to myself and a bother to others. Allowing myself to get that upset served no purpose.

I know now that I can't let myself respond in such a manner every time I see tragic news on television. While I never want to become indifferent to the suffering of others, I know that I can't function if I dive headlong into the pain of the entire world. I need to maintain some sort of emotional boundary.

I don't like having emotional meltdowns in front of others. Although my husband knows how much I struggle with my emotions, most people don't have a clue. "You're doing so well," I hear them say. "You keep your house so clean. Your gardens look so beautiful. You dress so nicely." And I can almost hear their unspoken thought: *Therefore, you have no problems.*

I often think how nice it would be to pop a pill to make my emotional pain go away. But I know that if I went down that path, my life could easily collapse under the weight of chemical dependency.

"You'll probably need to be on medication," one of my rehab therapists told me shortly after my injury. She couldn't imagine me being able to cope with the challenges of my injury on my own. I'm sure that if I reported my emotional problems to any doctor, he or she would readily prescribe a pharmaceutical aid. I am not saying this wouldn't be a legitimate option, and I never would discourage others from choosing to use psychotropic medication.

However, I know from past experience that antidepressant medication creates intolerable side effects for me, misery that outweighs any benefits the drug might provide. I know that antianxiety medication, the benzodiazepines, would, in the short run, ease my discomfort. But I also know that such drugs can be highly addictive. Moreover, I don't want to further cloud my dazed brain with the side effects of such medication. I want to remain as clear-minded as possible.

Still, the temptation to go down that road is there. I now have a better understanding of those who fall into addiction through self-medicating with drugs. Many of us are a hair's breadth away from that scenario.

At times, I have resorted to using antianxiety and antidepressant remedies provided by my naturopathic doctor, although their effects are subtle. You cannot hide inside the natural remedies the way you can with a benzodiazepine or an opioid medication.

So, I've had no good option for managing my emotions other than applying every coping strategy I can think of.

Since the day of my accident, I've had to do intensive psychotherapy on myself. I do a great deal of self-talk, giving myself the same advice I gave to clients during my years as a therapist. I find that speaking aloud as I coach myself through difficult situations is a powerful tool, more effective than just talking to myself in my mind.

I have come to learn the importance of monitoring and controlling my thoughts. I've noticed that whenever I have a negative thought about being inferior, inadequate, or bad, it rumbles through my being in a devastating way, like a shock wave. It makes me feel sick. Sometimes, I correct this by speaking aloud a counterthought to get myself back into balance.

When negative rumination gets the upper hand, I attempt to drown out the thoughts by singing a comforting song in my head, or repeating a spiritual mantra. Another remedy is to offer a prayer of gratitude for all the blessings I have in my life.

While I believe that confiding in those you trust can be beneficial in maintaining good mental health, I have come to understand the value of discretion. From painful experience, I have learned the futility of confiding in someone who is unable or unwilling to provide empathy. I have learned that when empathy from others isn't forthcoming, it is important to be my own friend, to empathize with myself.

So, when I have no one to talk to, or if confiding in another person would be inadvisable, I talk with myself about what I'm struggling with. Being completely honest regarding what is going on, no matter how petty, silly, or embarrassing the matter might be, helps my troubled feelings to pass more quickly. Accepting the feelings and breathing into them also helps. If I try to avoid them or push them away, they hang on more tenaciously.

In April 2017, I learned that a friend was going through a horrendous ordeal with bedbugs in his apartment. I felt terrible for him, and walked around for days feeling burdened down by sadness. When I realized what was causing my distress, I said aloud, "I am sad about the bedbugs." Then I talked with myself for a minute about what I was feeling, and my mood lightened.

Knowing how easily I can be triggered, I am learning to pull back before responding to something that angers me. I know from experience that expressing anger to others sometimes elicits a backlash that I can't handle. Most of the time, when I've calmed down, I realize the matter is not important, and that it is best to let it pass without any response.

However, while keeping my mouth shut often seems like the safest option, such a practice can lead to festering resentment. Sometimes, the best choice is speaking up and expressing the truth about what I'm feeling. Sometimes, it is imperative that I stand up for myself. I am constantly trying to discern when to keep quiet and when to speak up.

I have suffered from a lifetime phobia of snakes. I don't like hearing about snakes or seeing pictures of snakes. If an image of a wriggling snake suddenly appears on a television program I'm watching, I close my eyes until it passes. Encountering a live snake sends me into hysterics. My worst nightmares are about snakes. I never could bear to live in a part of the country that has a large population of snakes.

One evening in October 2017, when I was attending a social event, a woman sitting next to me began telling a story about a snake that crawled into someone's sleeping bag. Agitation instantly replaced my peaceful state of mind, and I recoiled in horror as she recounted the gruesome details.

I tried to listen politely, mentally willing the woman to wrap up her anecdote, but the creepy story dragged on and on. My agitation turned to anger, and I became more enraged by the minute. I wanted to reach over and throttle her.

After she was done talking, I told the woman how much her story had upset me. Unmoved by my distress, she responded with a flippant comment. I had to bite my tongue to keep from lashing out at her.

I went home that evening still feeling angry, desperately searching my mind for the reason this woman and her story had so riled me. Then, an odd memory came to me. During my childhood, a friend of our family had a penchant for telling tales that I experienced as creepy and unsettling. I had hated hearing his stories, but had never wanted to appear disrespectful. So, I'd suffered through them as a captive audience. All these years later, memories of those stories still haunt me.

After reflecting on this, I realized that the child me could have defended herself by walking away when such stories were being told. I also realized that the adult me could have protected herself by leaving the room when the woman started telling her snake story. In such a scenario, standing up for myself would have entailed action rather than a verbal confrontation.

My reflection led me to feeling kindlier toward the snake-story woman. She had been using her frightening tale to make a valid point. She had a right to tell that story. But I also had a right to protect myself from hearing it. Understanding that I can embolden myself to walk out of distressing situations makes me feel less angry and more empowered.

At those times when anger seems to take hold of my entire being, infiltrating every cell of my body, I know that I am in no condition to communicate with any other person. It is time for the big release, something to be done in private. When no one else is around to be disturbed by my outburst, I resort to screaming out my feelings while pounding on something, being as ugly and profane as I need to be. It is an exercise that invariably proves to be effective in decreasing my distress.

My tendency to push myself too hard, telling myself that I should be able to handle difficult situations, has often led me to people and places that create turmoil for me. After seven post-injury years of causing myself unnecessary suffering, I'm beginning to realize that it is time to do things differently. I have resolved that if the activity I'm doing or the company I'm keeping has repeatedly proven to cause me emotional distress, then it is time to let go. I am learning to avoid situations that present obvious triggers for painful emotions, unless there is a compelling reason for me to endure that difficulty.

I attend a meditation group that meets in a room at a local library. Overall, I find it to be a worthwhile and uplifting experience. But one day in March 2017, our library room was reserved for another gathering, so our meditation group had to meet elsewhere. The alternate venue turned out to be a place where I'd formerly been employed, a job that had been fraught with trauma. I'd left that position after only five months, as the circumstances there had been intolerable for me.

I knew that if I went back to that old place of employment, painful memories would be triggered. I'd inevitably encounter old ghosts in the building.

That week was already shaping up to be a rough one. I was going through the mental strain of releasing a new book. I was also scheduled to see my eye surgeon, and was experiencing considerable anxiety about that appointment.

So, I opted not to go to the meditation group that evening. With everything else that was going on, it wasn't the time to face traumatic memories. In the past, I would have told myself not to be a baby, to buck up and deal with challenges like this. But I knew that facing painful memories in a weakened emotional state would put me on a downward spiral, and that it would take me considerable time to recover.

Two months later, my meditation group again met at my former place of employment. This time, however, I was well-rested and in a calmer state of mind. So, I attended the meeting and faced the memories without undue suffering.

A few years after my injury, I attempted to broaden my community involvement by joining a group convened for the purpose of discussing social justice issues.

Ironically, I noticed early on that there was a social justice problem within the group. Certain group members, primarily male, dominated the group discussion, while others, primarily female, were sidelined. Because no one else in attendance seemed to be concerned about the matter, I decided to wait and see what would happen over time.

The first two times I attended the group meeting, I succeeded in managing my discomfort. But the third time, I happened to sit next to a man who fell asleep the minute the meeting started. He proceeded to snore loudly for the next hour. It began to feel like he was snoring directly into my ear. As the evening passed, this unpleasant sensory stimulation grew increasingly intolerable for me.

I wanted very much to participate in the group discussion, which had to do with the rights of gays and lesbians. But two men dominated the conversation, allowing no room for anyone else to jump in, essentially engaging in a dialog with each other.

Finally, I found an opportunity to offer my input. But I'd spoken only two or three sentences before one of the domineering men cut me off, attempting to regain control over the discussion.

My nerves were so on edge, from both the snoring and the unjust discussion of justice, that I spoke a little too sharply to my interrupter. "Wait a minute," I told him. "I'm not done."

Then I proceeded to speak two or three more sentences, although I was so shaken that the thoughts I was trying to express were undoubtedly incoherent. The interrupting man waited until I was done before he grabbed the floor again, promptly discounting what I'd just said.

Seething with anger, I sat in that meeting for another twenty minutes before I finally excused myself and left. I was afraid that if I stayed longer, I would embarrass myself by losing my temper.

I knew full well that rudeness in group discussions was a commonplace experience, and that the group had probably gotten out of hand many times before I ever joined it. I tried to talk reason to myself, but to no avail. I was livid.

I knew that my brain injury was partially responsible for my over-the-top emotions. But I sensed there was something deeper underlying my strong feelings. That night, I lay in bed unable to sleep, trying to make sense of what I'd just been through. And I realized that males sidelining females in conversations, interrupting them and discounting their thoughts, was part of my growing up environment. This happened both in my home and in my church, and later, in the workforce. Confident in their superiority, these men had taken for granted that their opinions were more important than those of their female counterparts.

I lay there that night feeling sympathy for the pain of all females who have felt diminished by men, coming to terms with how much it hurts to be treated like a second-class citizen. I then felt the need to extend my compassion to all individuals who have been marginalized in our society because of race, religion, sexual orientation, disability, or any other characteristic that sets them apart.

I terminated my involvement with the discussion group, resolving never to knowingly put myself in such a situation again. I knew I had lived through enough of that type of pain.

Spiritual practices and the contemplation of spiritual truths, both from my Christian upbringing and the eastern religions I have studied, help bring me back into balance when I am emotionally overwrought. It helps to remind myself that I am not the only one who suffers from emotional distress. Often, when I pray for divine assistance during my emotional struggles, I also pray for anyone else in the world who is suffering from similar pain. Doing so keeps me from becoming too self-centered in my suffering. I have found that such a practice brings surprising comfort.

I often think about the gems of wisdom imparted by the spiritual director of the ashram where I studied Vedantic scripture. Many times, I listened to him talk about the concept of detachment. He taught his students that our human lives will always be marked by ups and downs, and that spirituality will not bring an end to life's trials. He urged us to let go of our attachment to the cycle of emotional highs and lows, to find happiness within ourselves rather than allowing our state of mind to be dictated by outer circumstances.

Like many people, I have sought highs in life: career success, recognition by others, material possessions, perfect relationships. But these fleeting highs are always followed by disappointment and loss. The concept of detachment is becoming increasingly important to me, as I find the rollercoaster of excitement and disillusionment, of ecstasy and devastation, to be harder and harder to ride. Instead, I seek to maintain a state of calm contentment.

When I am emotionally shaken, I find solace in the routine activities of my life. I am learning to tolerate, even to appreciate, a little bit of boredom. It allows me to sleep at night.

I have discovered that what looks like depression or anxiety is often simply exhaustion. I have learned that any form of brain strain can morph into an emotional problem. When my brain gets tired, everything starts to fall apart, and my mind goes haywire. The only remedy is rest.

At the appointment with my eye surgeon in March 2017, I endured intrusive procedures involving bright lights being shined directly into my dilated eyes. Afterwards, I was besieged by wild, fearful thoughts and weird, out-of-control emotions. Thankfully, I realized that this strange phenomenon was due to the brain strain I'd been through. I knew the only thing to do was to rest and give my brain a break until the experience passed.

I also cope with my fragile emotions by focusing on eating right. I have struggled all my adult life with hypoglycemia, which, if not managed properly, adds to my emotional difficulties. I use exercise to help stabilize my moods.

I find that spending time in nature is one of the best antidepressants available to me, just as effective as anything that comes in a pill form. Taking walks in nature never fails to lift my mood. I've learned that even on days when my life seems unmanageable and unbearable, working in my flowerbeds is an experience worth staying alive for.

During extremely cold or extremely hot weather, it becomes harder to get my time in nature. But I've discovered something magical about an early morning in the dead of summer. There is a window of bliss that I can seize before the ferocious heat of the day drives me indoors.

Another remedy I sometimes use when overcome by depression or anxiety is a warm or cold compress on my body. A warm compress brings comfort when I'm feeling sad and depleted, while a cold pack can shock my body out of a state of extreme agitation.

I know that what I watch on TV can easily take me down. Horror movies are completely off limits for me. Particularly when I'm feeling emotionally vulnerable, I am unable to handle anything depicting crime and violence. My brain goes careening off into self-inflicted anxiety, my mind racing with fearful thoughts.

After hearing the results of the national election in November 2016, I grew more frantic by the hour. I was overdosing on television news, and had also gotten caught up in the hysteria on social media. I unwisely attempted to confide my feelings in several well-meaning friends, who preached at me not to be upset. This, of course, only made me feel worse.

I was so off-balance that I misjudged the space while backing out of my garage, scraping my car's side-view mirror. Nothing I attempted to do around the house was turning out well. My fingernails were breaking off. My new conditioner made my hair feel greasy. I'd recently lost weight, and felt pitiful in my ill-fitting clothing. My entire world felt out of control.

I finally stepped back from the turmoil in my life and took stock of what was happening to me. I realized it was time to stop agitating myself with the news on television and the pandemonium on Facebook. It was time to avoid phone calls and to delete emotionally charged emails I didn't want to read. Shutting out the external bombardment, I listened to soothing music to quiet my mind and to reconnect with my true self in the middle of all the chaos.

To all those with a loved-one who experiences emotional suffering related to a brain injury, I urge you to respond to them with compassion. Don't scold, judge, or humiliate them. Don't make light of their difficulties. Understand that their pain is real. Help your injured loved-ones develop coping skills.

I also ask for compassion for anyone who suffers emotionally, be it from mental illness, a history of trauma, or simply being endowed with a sensitive temperament.

One night when I lay awake in a state of emotional turmoil, I thought about all the people who've ever said to me, "You're so strong," or, "You're doing so well." I knew they would be surprised to know how much I was struggling at that moment.

Then I thought about my late father. He was always a rock-like structure in my life, always trustworthy, never shirking his responsibilities. By all appearances, he was a strong man. He rarely revealed vulnerable feelings, and most people would not think of him as someone who struggled emotionally.

But as I grew older, I began to understand that my father was a compassionate person who was moved by the pain of others. I saw that criticism wounded him deeply. I saw that stress wore him down, and that his emotional sensitivity caused him a great deal of quiet suffering.

I regretted that I'd never provided my strong, steadfast father with emotional support. So I spoke to him that night. I told him that not only did I see his strength, I saw his suffering. I told him that he deserved compassion and understanding, of which he'd received little in his lifetime. I told him I was sorry that I had not provided this when he was alive.

Offering that empathy warmed my heart and calmed my agitated spirit. I hope that, somehow, my father heard me.

FEARING THE FEAR

Anxiety feels terrible. It grabs you in its wicked jaws and shakes you mercilessly. It creates unbearable physiological symptoms. It is responsible for many trips to the emergency room. Sometimes, it makes you think you are dying.

The neuropsychologist who worked with me the first year after my injury said something that proved to be true in my case. "Whatever a person is like prior to a brain injury," he told me, "they're even more like that after the injury."

In other words, if you're outspoken prior to your injury, you'll be even more outspoken afterwards. If you are quiet, you'll be quieter after your injury. If you have problems with anxiety, that anxiety will be magnified after your injury.

Certainly, I struggled with anxiety prior to my injury. I was a worrier, a perfectionist, always fearful that I would be judged for performing poorly in some area of my life. But my brain injury, coupled with all the trauma that followed the accident, left every molecule in my body riddled with anxiety.

In the first few years after my injury, I had numerous medical evaluations and treatments that were difficult to endure. These included three neuropsychological evaluations, several brain scans, physical, occupational, and speech therapy, months of cognitive rehabilitation sessions, multiple eye exams involving intrusive procedures, and half a year of vision therapy. I'd never before been afraid of doctors, but upsetting encounters with medical professionals after my injury made me begin to fear medical appointments of any kind. Facing any type of evaluation triggered paranoia.

When I enrolled in my new health insurance plan in January 2017, I learned that one of the benefits of the plan was an in-home assessment by the company's physician. Some months later, I received a call informing me that the doctor was going to be in my community that week. I was asked if I wanted to set up a time for him to come to my home.

Reluctantly, I scheduled the appointment. But the minute I hung up the phone, I went into a panic. I had no idea who would show up on my doorstep. I had no idea what he would do or say to me. I couldn't stand the idea of being alone in my house with this unknown doctor.

My husband tried to assure me that it would be okay. But I knew that dreading the doctor's knock on my door would ruin my entire day, if not my entire week. So, I called the insurance company and canceled the appointment.

In addition to experiencing trauma with medical professionals, the first three years after my accident were marked by a contentious relationship with the auto insurance company responsible for paying my medical bills. I also faced the inordinate strain of dealing with several lawsuits. My husband and I never would have pursued these lawsuits allowed by Michigan law, if it were not for the fact that we otherwise would have faced financial ruin.

Such matters never had been part of my life before. My attorney informed me that going through such lawsuits was difficult for sensitive people. He was right. They were horrendous to deal with, particularly in my compromised mental state.

Because I had to participate in so many phone conversations that overwhelmed and frightened me, and because I often felt threatened by the contents of legal and insurance letters that came in the mail, I developed fears that I'd never had to contend with before. Every time the phone rang, my heart pounded, as I was sure I was about to hear some ominous news. Each day around one o'clock, when the mail was due to arrive, I would experience a sense of foreboding.

The adversarial nature of my insurance and legal problems made me feel as if I was being scrutinized and judged, as if insurance companies and law firms were zeroing in on me as a target. As if it was me, not the driver of the car who'd hit me, who had done something wrong. I lived with a constant feeling of being in trouble. I didn't even know what terrible things I might have done, but I feared the insurance company's attorneys would find something to pin on me.

After three years of dealing with these problems, the lawsuits were finally settled and my case with the auto insurance company was closed. I breathed a huge sigh of relief, believing that terrible chapter of my life was behind me, hoping that I'd never need to live through such an ordeal again. But several years later, I received the startling letter from my health insurance company telling me they were going after my former auto insurance to pay for my 2014 back surgery.

I had a horrible feeling of being sucked back into the maelstrom of conflict and harassment, of being faced with one threat after another. As I stood there holding that letter in my hand, I wanted to die. Death seemed preferable to reliving those years of trauma.

Over the next six months, several more of those ominous letters arrived in the mail. Forcing myself to buck up and push through my fear, I made numerous phone calls to clarify the matter before finally convincing myself that the problem posed no threat to me. Thankfully, the letters finally stopped coming.

I know that I've developed post-traumatic stress symptoms related to my accident, and to those years of contending with insurance and legal problems. I feel a great deal of compassion for people whose post-traumatic stress disorder is worse than mine, who experience more crippling symptoms than I have to contend with. It's a rough way to live.

My fears have sometimes become self-centered, as I've often felt as if I was the only one in the world dealing with insurance and legal problems. I had a much-needed reality check when I received a letter from my friend Roseanne, in which she detailed her challenges in signing up for a new health insurance plan. The company's errors and the miscommunication between her and the insurance agents nearly drove her out of her mind. I thanked her for telling me that story, as it reminded me that dealing with bureaucracy and large companies is a messy, frustrating, and contentious process for everyone.

Anxiety is now my most difficult emotional state to deal with. As do many other anxious people, I've come to a point where I dread future episodes of anxiety. The fear of the anxiety has become almost as bad as the anxiety itself.

While I have spells of depression, they come and go. Anxiety has a more tenacious hold on me. Overstimulation easily triggers anxiety, and just a bit too much brain strain can turn me into a nervous wreck.

But I also struggle with a generalized anxiety that comes from feeling so vulnerable in my brain-injured state. I am afraid of not being able to stand up to life's demands. I've always struggled with fears of inadequacy, but since my injury, it is so much more difficult to measure up, to be "good enough."

When I began working with Michigan Rehabilitation Services (MRS), I had no idea how complicated my involvement with them would be. I had to cope with multiple changes in workers, referrals to other agencies that didn't pan out, and a great deal of miscommunication. I never quite knew what was expected of me, or what I needed to do next. I developed paranoia about meetings with my workers, fearing that I would be castigated for not doing well enough.

The fears associated with working with MRS tormented me for several years. I was afraid the goals set for me were out of my reach, and that those who worked with me would see me as an abysmal failure. I didn't believe I deserved the resources the agency spent in working with me. I'd sit alone in my house contemplating my inadequacies, overcome by anxiety and shame.

One day in July 2016, as I ruminated on my perceived failure in reaching MRS goals, I heard words in my mind that didn't seem to be entirely mine: *I see a lot of work ahead of me. I am willing to do it, but periods of work must be interspersed with periods of rest.*

I'd never had such a thought before. I suddenly saw that I had allowed myself to become so exhausted from my work with MRS that I had ended up feeling beleaguered and overwhelmed.

At times when fears of inadequacy and failure have threatened to choke the life out of me, my best consolation has been a truth I learned from the spiritual director of the ashram where I studied Vedantic scripture. He taught us students to do our work as if it is an offering to God, then to detach from the results of the work. "The work is yours," he'd say, "and the results are God's."

So, time and again, I pulled myself out of my fearful paralysis and addressed the next step MRS had set in front of me, knowing that I had no control over the outcome of my efforts.

In publishing my first few books, Russ and I encountered a daunting learning curve as we struggled with formatting the books' interiors and creating the covers.

In the summer of 2014, we labored for weeks over the cover of my third book, *Rachel's Song.* We grew increasingly frustrated with the project. But one Saturday morning in July, we came to a point of breakthrough. We approved our final product, then ordered a supply of books.

At first, I felt relief and joy that we had finally accomplished what we'd set out to do. That afternoon, I spent some time doing Tai Chi in my backyard, gazing at my flower gardens with blissful eyes. I felt at peace with the world.

But in the evening, I experienced a violent emotional crash. I suddenly became fearful that the book cover would be defective, and that I would have approved the distribution of a book that was sub-par. I imagined opening the box of books we'd ordered, only to find the front cover image badly distorted.

The irrational fear gripped me so hard that I couldn't sleep that night. My anxiety colored everything in my life. I felt like a horrible, doomed human being. As I was so exhausted on Sunday, the fear continued its hold on me. In the late afternoon, Russ and I walked down to Lake Michigan, where I engaged in my tried and true remedy for calming myself: wading in the water.

Feeling more rested on Monday and Tuesday, I was able to contemplate why the crash had occurred. In addition to working hard on the book cover on Saturday, I had pushed myself too far with my writing. I had simply engaged in too much brain strain, overloading my fragile circuits. While this type of brain meltdown had happened multiple times since my injury, I had never crashed as violently as I did that Saturday.

A few days after that massive meltdown, I received the shipment of books we'd ordered. With great apprehension, I tore open the box. To my profound relief, the cover looked beautiful, and I felt silly for having gotten so worked up. I hoped I had learned a lesson about pointless anxiety.

But I also realized that the thought of releasing a defective book tapped into deep-seated fears from my childhood. Fear of judgment and punishment for imperfection had been deeply entrenched in my young psyche.

A great deal of dread and doom had been embedded in my early religious teachings. I was taught to be terrified of God. My strict, pious mother, who didn't hesitate to control her children through fear, instilled in me the belief that the second coming of Christ could occur at any moment. She told me that if I was caught in the act of wrongdoing at such a time, or that if I had failed to ask for God's forgiveness for some past transgression, I would go to hell.

Hell, of course, meant being consumed by a fire that never stopped burning for all of eternity. I couldn't imagine such pain, such torment. The thought of hell made me constantly insecure, questioning every move I made. In my mind, any small infraction, any imperfection, could have dire consequences, even eternal consequences.

When I was in fifth grade, I was terrified of my teacher, Mr. Bainter. He tolerated no nonsense, and was known for his short fuse. From time to time, I'd see him explode in anger at one of my classmates. I had no desire to be on the receiving end of his temper.

One day, Mr. Bainter offered us students the opportunity to earn extra credit by memorizing a lengthy poem. Those of us who took advantage of the offer had to stand at his desk and recite the poem to him.

When it came my turn to recite the poem, Mr. Bainter acknowledged that I had done so correctly, and I received the appropriate credit for my effort. But when I went back to my desk and looked at the poem again, I realized I had made a tiny error. I had substituted "a" for "the" at one point in my recitation.

Sick at heart, I was sure I had received credit fraudulently. I worried for the rest of the day. The next morning, I woke up still worried, believing myself to be a cheat and a liar. I was caught in a dilemma between two terrifying entities, Mr. Bainter and God. If I confessed my error to Mr. Bainter, I might incur his terrible anger. But I never could hide my secret from God, who was even scarier than my teacher. I was sure that failure to make things right could send me to hell.

So, when I arrived at school, I approached Mr. Bainter's

desk with trepidation, carrying a copy of the poem. I pointed out to him where I had made my mistake, then held my breath while I awaited his response. I was sure he would turn on me in a rage.

To my utter surprise, he spoke with kindness. "It's okay," he said. And that was all. The terrible matter was over.

Looking back, I am astounded by the burden of fear and guilt I carried as a child. My heart truly wants to release the pain of believing that I need to be perfect, and that I will be punished if I fail to do so. I don't fully know how to let those fears go. But I trust the change will come in time, probably in increments.

While the wisest part of me knows the event that caused my brain injury was purely accidental, and that the driver had no intention of assaulting me, being hit by a car has sometimes felt like a personal attack.

Once when absorbed with such thoughts, I recalled an incident from decades earlier. When my children were little, I had a child seat on the back of my bicycle, and would frequently take them out for rides. One day, I strapped four-year-old Zane into the child seat, and we headed downtown to run an errand. As we passed an alley, a truck pulled out and hit us. It barely bumped us, just enough to knock us over, and neither Zane nor I were injured.

Terrified about what he'd done, the driver jumped out of the truck to see if we were okay. He apologized profusely. I assured him that we were fine. Stunned and frightened, little Zane said only one thing to the man. "Why did you do this?" he whimpered. He couldn't conceive of that event as being an accident. It felt like a personal assault to him.

Since incurring my brain injury, I have struggled with a nagging fear of being blindsided by another unanticipated tragedy. It's as if I am constantly waiting for the other shoe to drop.

I know this fear of impending tragedy also taps into the belief system of my childhood. Not only was I taught to be terrified of punishment by God, I grew up during the cold war, under the imminent threat of an attack by the Soviet Union. My mother instilled in me the worry that, at any moment, the Russians could overrun our country and take away all our rights.

She insisted that my siblings and I memorize a quota of Bible verses every morning, so that if the communists came and took away our Bibles, we would have the scripture stored in our minds.

One day when I was in elementary school, I was in our backyard with my mother, helping her hang laundry on the clothesline. We'd just had a conversation about the Russians, and a feeling of dread churned in the pit of my stomach. "What will we do if the Russians bomb Beanblossom?" I asked her.

"They won't bomb a little place like Beanblossom," she assured me. "They'll just bomb big cities like Indianapolis."

That was a bit of consolation for me, and I breathed easier for a minute or two. Still, I knew Indianapolis was only an hour away from where we lived.

After being hit by a car, those long-buried childhood fears of impending doom leaped forward, feelings I'd thought the grownup me had mastered. It seemed as if some defense mechanism had crumbled, leaving me staring into the face of childhood terror.

One breathtakingly gorgeous summer day in 2016, I was about to pull out of the parking lot of my medical exercise program, ready to embark upon the four-mile drive home. I paused for a moment, allowing myself to be enthralled by the perfection of the day. But as I took in the splendor, a dark thought crept in, chasing away my joy: *I wonder if I will make it home without a mishap.*

The thought was followed by profound sadness. Why couldn't I enjoy moments of beauty, even if they were fleeting? Why couldn't I experience joy without a foreboding sense that tragedy was knocking at my door?

In the darkest times since my injury, I've fallen into thinking that all I can expect for the remainder of my life is doom. And when something unfortunate does happen, I've taken it as confirmation that only bad things are lurking in the shadows of my life, monsters waiting to jump out and snatch me.

I've had to start all over in terms of learning to believe that good fortune can still come my way, that pleasant things, not just tragedy, can happen to me by surprise. While I know there will still be difficult events in my future, I don't want to miss out on joy because I am so riddled with fear.

I often try to calm my fears by thinking back on times when good fortune took me by surprise. One event always stands out to me, something that happened while I was attending graduate school.

I had completed one year of college prior to marrying my first husband Larry. Then, after my three children were born, I resumed my college career, attending classes part-time while juggling the responsibilities of caring for my family. When, after many years of being a part-time student, I finally received my undergraduate degree, I was determined to go straight on to graduate school. The idea seemed daunting, but Larry and I cobbled together a viable plan.

Based on my undergraduate performance, the graduate program invited me to apply for a grant, a sum of money that would make my academic venture financially easier on our household. But there were candidates with more impressive credentials ahead of me on the list, and I was not awarded the grant. My husband and I had to continue making our plans without counting on that additional source of money.

In the early weeks of my first semester of graduate school, I was sitting in a classroom when the dean suddenly appeared in the doorway. He was strikingly eccentric in appearance, a short fellow with a round belly, plaid pants, and a glorious white beard. He announced to my professor that he needed to speak to me.

Bewildered, I left the classroom and followed this colorful character out into the hallway. My heart pounded in fear as he stood there peering at me through his thick glasses. Then, he proceeded to inform me that one of the grant recipients had dropped out of school, that my name had been next on the list, and that I had just been awarded five thousand dollars to help with my graduate school expenses.

"Five ... thousand ... bucks!" he intoned in a resonant voice.

My fear changed to elation. It felt as if fate was beaming the sunniest of smiles on me.

As it turned out, Larry and I had underestimated how much graduate school was going to cost, and we would have been in dire straits without that grant money. The extra five thousand dollars filled in our financial gaps perfectly.

In the aftermath of my injury, I've thought about that story many times, reminding myself to look at ways things have turned out in recent years. Despite the trauma, the turmoil, and the financial threats, Russ and I have not gone hungry or lost our home. We've managed to pay our bills, even though Russ was laid off from a job and went through several months of unemployment. In countless little ways, things have come together in perfect timing.

One day when I was obsessing about the things I fear, I wondered whether I'd ever look back and notice how irrational those fears had been, how pointless it had been to waste time on them. And I suddenly remembered a story from my childhood.

When I was about to enter first grade, my brother Earl, who was a teenager at the time, couldn't resist tormenting his little sister by planting a fear in her mind. He told me that if I ever talked to a boy at school, or even sat next to a boy, then that fellow would be my boyfriend.

In my six-year-old mind, being saddled with a boyfriend was an unappealing idea. Determined to avoid such a fate, I made sure to steer clear of the boys in my classroom. Each afternoon when I came home from school, Earl would interrogate me: "Did you talk to a boy today? Did you sit by a boy?" And I would assure him that I hadn't.

As I became acclimated to my classroom, one particular student struck me as odd. He was a head taller than the rest of us first graders, and in my opinion, he was decidedly weird-looking. He also had a weird name: Willis Walls.

Later, I came to understand that Willis Walls was a foster child, and that he suffered from mild mental retardation. As our school did not have a special education program, there was no option for dealing with a slow learner other than having him repeat the grades he failed to master. Thus, Willis Walls was two years older than his classmates.

But as a six-year-old, I didn't know all this. In my mind, Willis Walls was just that strange-looking, oversized boy who sat in the back of the room and behaved in ways I thought were odd.

When I announced to my family that I had a weird kid in my class, I quickly regretted my mistake. Never missing an opportunity to torment his little sister, Earl promptly informed me that Willis Walls was, now and forever, my boyfriend. He, along with the rest of my siblings, teased me about Willis mercilessly.

Throughout my elementary school years, Willis Walls was a fixture in my classroom. The unfortunate child was an easy target for bullying, and was often the butt of his classmates' jokes. At home, my brothers and sisters teased me about my so-called boyfriend for years. Because of this, Willis Walls became repugnant to me.

Every year at Christmastime, my elementary school class would draw names for a gift exchange. The last day before our holiday break, we'd have a party, at which time the gifts would be handed out.

When I was in fifth grade, something happened that turned my holiday excitement into a nightmare. When I plucked the slip of paper from the bowl on name-drawing day, I recoiled in horror when I read what was on it. I had drawn Willis Walls' name.

Now, I would be forced to do something nice for a boy I couldn't stand. I knew this was going to provide more fodder for teasing by my siblings. They would insist that my buying a gift for Willis Walls was undeniable evidence that I was in love with him. I also imagined that my classmates would taunt me when Willis opened his gift from me in front of all of them.

But I dutifully bought Willis a gift, and I survived the humiliating ordeal of gift-opening day. It turned out to be nothing compared to what happened a few months later.

On a Saturday morning in May, I overheard my father talking to my mother about a woman who had invited him to come to her home and harvest rhubarb from her garden. I had no idea who she was. My mother enjoyed making rhubarb pies, so my parents decided to take advantage of the offer.

As my father prepared to drive to the home of the rhubarb-growing woman, he asked my little sister Barbara and me if we wanted to come along. I was eleven at the time, and Barbara, a giggly little pest, was almost six.

When we pulled into the rhubarb lady's driveway, the door of the house opened and a boy stepped out. I could not believe my eyes. It was Willis Walls. The rhubarb lady was his foster mother.

For one appalling moment, Willis and I locked eyes. I stared at him in horror, and he stared back at me, bewildered, as if he couldn't figure out why I was there.

I was mortified. There I was, at the home of the boy I detested above all others. Then my shock turned to anger. I was furious with my dad. If I had known where we were going, I never would have agreed to ride along with him. I felt as if I'd been set up for humiliation.

I was not about to exit the car until Willis walked away. Fortunately for me, he accompanied my father to the rhubarb patch. His foster mother, Mrs. Wade, invited Barbara and me to sit with her under a shade tree in her yard while my father harvested the rhubarb.

I sat there in an outraged silence as Mrs. Wade prattled nonsense, and I quickly determined that she was as weird as her foster son. When a sudden breeze raised goosebumps on our arms, she glanced up at the sky and said, "It's getting chilly. I wonder if it's going to snow."

At that moment, I decided that Mrs. Wade was completely out of her mind. I knew full well that it never snowed in May where we lived in southern Indiana. There I was, stuck at the home of two crazy people, living out a horror story that I wanted no one else to know about. If word ever got out that I'd been to Willis Walls' house, I'd never be able to live it down. I couldn't wait for my dad to get done with the rhubarb so that we could tear out of there and never look back.

Now, I had two black marks on my record. Not only had I bought Willis Walls a gift at Christmastime, I'd visited his home. Now, there were two pieces of incontrovertible evidence that I had a special relationship with the repugnant fellow.

After the harrowing incident, I took my little sister aside, making her promise that she'd never tell any of my friends that I'd been to Willis Walls' home. Of course, Barbara never held to any such promise. Whenever my friends were around, she would start giggling, and I'd know what was about to come. When she'd blurt out, "Guess what Lois did," I'd tackle her and clamp my hand over her mouth before she could announce my shame to the entire world.

All that summer, I lived in fear that Barbara would reveal my ugly secret to my friends. In my mind, she had the capability of completely ruining my eleven-year-old reputation. That possibility hung over me like a dark cloud, casting a shadow over my entire life.

Looking back, I laugh at my childish fears. No one, except for my teasing siblings, cared that I went to Willis Walls' house. No one else gave the matter a minute of thought. My worry, my self-torture, had all been for nothing.

By sixth grade, Willis Walls was gone, perhaps to another foster home in another community. My fear of being teased about him faded, only to be replaced by another fear.

As a preteen, I was a tomboy. I enjoyed playing sports, especially softball. Every recess, my school friends and I would race to the ball diamond, never getting our fill of the game.

One of my classmates, Freddie Miller, was my sports buddy. That is, until one fateful day during sixth grade when I caught a fly ball that he hit. After that, he hated me.

Shortly after that event, my teacher set up a word-game contest for us students. She announced that the prize would be a box of chocolate-covered grasshoppers. I'd never heard of such a novelty. I applied every ounce of my concentration to winning that contest, and was thrilled when my teacher handed the box of chocolate-covered insects to me.

After sampling one piece of the candy, I realized it wasn't the delicacy I'd hoped it would be. Those grasshoppers tasted vile. Not only that, they brought a curse upon my life. They gave Freddie Miller the perfect opportunity to get revenge on me for catching his fly ball. The minute I won the prize, he dubbed me "Grasshopper."

Every time I came into their line of vision, Freddie and his pals would shriek, "Gra-a-asss-hopper!" in a high-pitched tone. I avoided Freddie as much as possible, but to no avail. Every day at school, I was bombarded by his hideous screams: "Grasshopper! Grasshopper!" I couldn't even get away from his torment at night. He shrieked "Grasshopper" at me in my dreams.

I became so scared of Freddie that I dreaded going to school. I became terrified of the boy who'd once been my friend, and my fearfulness only encouraged his bullying behavior. The name "Grasshopper" seemed to follow me everywhere I went for the rest of my sixth-grade year.

Thankfully, I had no classes with Freddie Miller in seventh grade, so my fear of hearing him scream out my ugly nickname dissipated. But new fears about fitting in with my peers came in its place. Then, high school fears replaced middle school fears. All my life, fears have come and gone, new ones arriving on the scene when old ones disappeared. Now, I'm contending with my post-injury fears.

I ask myself whether all these fears are worth the mental energy they've cost me. I know there is no point to any of this self-inflicted misery, but I'm still working on convincing myself of that fact.

I have sometimes heard it said that the things we worry about the most are not the tragedies that actually befall us. Interestingly, I had never worried about the possibility of getting hit by a car. I'm glad I didn't, as that fear would have ruined precious hours of my life.

I'm quite sure that when I look back someday, my current fears will seem as silly as my childhood fears about Willis Walls and Freddie Miller.

Overcoming anxiety will probably be a project I work on for the rest of my life. Whenever irrational fears grab hold of me, I try to look at them dispassionately, to not take them too seriously. It helps to remember that anxiety is a feature of the human condition that millions of other people share with me.

CAT MAMA

All of us know what it's like to feel regret after making a bad decision. We've all had times of ruminating over foolish things we've done, berating ourselves for our errors in judgment. But, being human, we tend to make the same poor decisions over and over again, until the lessons embedded in those experiences finally sink in.

At different points in my life, I've made decisions that resulted in such painful consequences that I've told myself, "You MUST learn from this mistake. You NEVER can repeat this course of action. If you do, you may not be able to recover from it the next time."

In the aftermath of my brain injury, I've discovered, more than ever, how important it is for me to learn from experience. The repercussions from poor choices result in overwhelming anxiety, downward emotional spirals, and cognitive meltdowns. I simply cannot cope with the pain from making the same mistakes again and again. Many times, I've had to tell myself, "You need to handle this situation differently than you did the last time. If you repeat your mistake, you know what the consequence will be. You don't want to face that again."

Sadly, one of my hardest post-injury lessons about decision-making had to do with cats.

I've put in a lot of years as a cat mama. A month after I married my first husband Larry, he and I bought a female Siamese kitten, whom I named Miranda.

In my mind, Miranda was my first child. I babied her ridiculously. I bought her a leash and a fancy collar and took her almost everywhere I went. I referred to her as my little girl, which confused people who didn't know I was talking about a cat.

When my first human baby was born, my feline baby became a lower priority in my life. Poor Miranda became jealous of the attention I gave little Zane. She stopped eating and grew very thin. She eventually regained her appetite and her weight, but her spirit never fully recovered.

As our family expanded to include a second child, we filled

every inch of our small house. I began to think we no longer had room for a cat. Miranda's food dishes and litterbox were constantly in the way, and I was concerned about maintaining a sanitary environment for my infant and toddler. So, we took Miranda to the animal shelter.

It was a valid decision at the time, but later, I regretted it. I couldn't stop wondering what fate had befallen the kitty that had been my first baby. My guilt was so overwhelming that I vowed never to give up on a pet again.

A dozen years of childrearing passed before another cat came into my life. Shortly after Larry and I divorced, my three children found an adorable black and white tuxedo kitten hanging around their father's house. They named him Vinnie.

Before I knew it, Vinnie was a member of my household. He was a year old at the time, and he stayed with me until his death at the age of twelve. My adolescent children doted on him and poked fun at his eccentric cat behavior. His greatest trick was jumping up and turning on the light switch in our hallway, which made all of us think he was brilliant. With my children's help, I began writing cat songs about him, a tradition I continued with subsequent pets. Our family still enjoys a considerable body of lore about Vinnie.

Shortly after Vinnie turned six, my youngest son Quinton, who was eighteen at the time, moved out of the house and into an apartment with roommates. His friend's cat had a litter of kittens, most of whom were quickly adopted into new households. One calico female seemed to be wanted by no one, and Quinton was afraid she would come to some unfortunate end. So, he claimed her as his own and named her Ziggy. As he was not allowed to have pets in his apartment, he begged me to provide Ziggy with temporary shelter until he could find a home where he could keep her.

I was not in the market for a second cat, but Quinton wore me down. So, I opened my home to a rambunctious kitten who terrorized poor Vinnie and made his life miserable. Quinton never did find a place where he could take her in, and I ended up keeping Ziggy until her death at eighteen. I often teased Quinton that Ziggy clung to life for so long because she was waiting for her daddy to come and take her home with him.

When Vinnie died in 2002, Ziggy was six. She remained my only cat for five months. I was then at the height of my career, feeling like an empowered woman able to provide myself with whatever I wanted. And what I was determined to get was a pedigreed cat.

At that point, I'd been married to Russ for two years. He and I researched different cat breeds on the internet. I wanted a lap cat, one I could baby like I'd babied Miranda. I identified two breeds that struck my fancy: Ragdoll cats and Ocicats.

We located a Ragdoll breeder an hour away from our home. When we contacted her, she informed us that she had a newborn litter. All but one of them, a male, had already been claimed. We immediately claimed the remaining kitten sight unseen, and as soon as we could, we set out on a trip to visit him.

I immediately fell in love with the eleven-ounce squealing ball of fluff. He was completely white at that point. We were told he would have the markings of a flame-point Ragdoll, with a pale orange color emerging on his face and paws as he grew older.

While I could hardly wait to take my new baby home with me, he was not yet old enough to be separated from his feline mother. The breeder told us he wouldn't be ready to live with us for another two months.

So, my husband and I had to go home without our baby. I spent the following weeks preparing for him, fantasizing about what it would be like to be the mama of this glorious kitten. I chose a name for him: Maven. I began writing cat songs about him even before he came to our house.

While we were waiting to bring Maven home, I was so enthused about pedigreed cats that I persuaded Russ to take me to a cat show in Kalamazoo, Michigan. And there, I came upon a four-month-old Ocicat. The little fellow, who sported chocolate spots on a background of sleek silver fur, was curled up with his sister and mother, sleeping peacefully. I immediately knew that I could never live without him.

Russ had stepped out of the building for a few minutes. I ran to get him, exclaiming, "Honey, come see what I found!" It didn't take much time to convince him that we needed to buy the little Ocicat right there on the spot.

Before his breeder handed the kitten over to me, she held him in her arms, wagged a finger in his face, and said, "You be a good boy now."

We immediately came up with a name for the kitten: King Leopold, Leo for short. We bought a cardboard cat carrier there at the show, stashed Leo in the back seat of the car, and set out for the fifty-mile trip home.

Within minutes, I knew that Leo had not listened to a word of his breeder's parting injunction. We had bought, not a kitten, but a cross between a jumping bean and the Energizer Bunny. He whined and begged to get out of his carrier. When we finally allowed him to do so, he bounced around the car, making it impossible for Russ to drive. We had to corral him again and put him back into temporary incarceration.

Twenty-four hours after we arrived home, Leo's hyperactive kitten behavior had so unnerved me that I was wailing, "Oh God, what have I done?" But my doubts quickly faded, as King Leopold swept me under his spell, rendering me a helpless victim of his charm.

Ziggy, however, was deeply offended that we had brought this demented little creature into our household. I could almost read her thoughts through her sulky eyes: *Was I not good enough for you?* But she grudgingly accepted Leo as her feline companion.

Ziggy's antics as a kitten paled in comparison to what Leo was capable of. He was a valiant jumper, able to land on unbelievably high surfaces. He had a habit of perching on the refrigerator or the top of a cupboard, then leaping down to land on our shoulders, scaring us half to death.

Still, Leo was a fantastic lap cat, which pleased me to no end. Both Vinnie and Ziggy had remained aloof to my overtures, preferring their independence to having their mama fawn over them. Leo allowed me to baby him to ridiculous lengths. He came to believe that any time a human being was in a seated or lying down position, he belonged on top of them. When my husband would come home from work and plop down in his recliner, Leo would immediately jump on his lap. Russ would point an accusing finger at me and say, "You created this."

Of course, I was prolific in writing cat songs about my

spotted little darling. Lyrics describing his amazing attributes were just about the only thing running through my mind.

By the time Maven arrived at our home, Leo had already claimed the title of Mama's One True Love. Of course, I loved Maven just as much, but I could never let Leo know that. Completely confident in his superior role in the household, Leo was unthreatened by Maven's arrival. He gave the newcomer a good sniffing and decided that he'd allow him to stay. So, the sleek brown-spotted kitten and the fluffy white kitten became friends for life.

But Ziggy let us know that we'd crossed the line with her. In her mind, there was no reason at all to bring a second little pest into her world. She became depressed, listless, and withdrawn, and did not recover her normal personality for a full year. And she never forgave Maven for ruining her life. She hated him with a passion, hissing any time he came near her.

The Ragdoll cat is a large breed, and Maven grew so rapidly that it scared me. He reminded me of the plant in the musical, "Little Shop of Horrors." Because he grew so large so quickly, his kitten behavior created catastrophes in the house. I'd tell Russ that Maven didn't make messes; he created crime scenes. I often thought I needed to cordon off an area of his handiwork with police tape.

Maven was not much of a lap cat, so he never threatened Leo's spot. But he liked to be near his humans, and tended to follow me around the house. When I'd get ready for work in the morning, doing my hair and makeup in the bathroom, Maven would hop on the vanity, where he'd sit and watch me.

He loved to follow me to the basement when I did laundry, but would insist that I carry him back up the stairs. This was a bit of a backbreaking feat, as in his prime, he topped the scale at twenty-two pounds. But I always agreed to his request, as holding Maven was a luxurious experience. The texture of his fur made me feel as if I was wrapping my arms around an expensive mink coat.

Maven knew how handsome he was. He had a way of strutting to show off his magnificence. Anyone who saw him for the first time would gasp at his beauty. He especially loved it when women at the vet's office fawned over him.

In the face of Leo and Maven's relentless bids for attention, poor Ziggy skulked in the shadows, asking for nothing besides food and a peaceful spot in which to sleep. Sadly, she must have accrued a great deal of bad kitty karma during the years she tormented Vinnie, as Leo and Maven loved to pester her. It seemed that Russ and I were constantly jumping in to protect her. But she learned to defend herself by throwing the most impressive hissy fits I'd ever seen.

For ten years, Russ and I enjoyed this wonderful trio of cats in our household. They loved, they fought, they entertained us, they demanded an inordinate amount of our time and energy. That decade was a special chapter of my life, one that can never be replicated. After my brain injury in 2010, the presence of my three feline darlings was a tremendous comfort to me.

But one year after my injury, my big beautiful Maven showed signs of serious illness. I was crushed. I had to begin facing the reality that my cats wouldn't last forever. As I was at a point where I could hardly take care of myself, caring for a sick cat was a daunting task. Over the next twelve months, Russ and I took Maven to countless veterinary appointments. We learned that he had both digestive and urinary track problems, and that he was in constant pain.

We tried different medications. But Maven was a sensitive cat who developed allergic reactions to routine vaccinations, and every shot or pill he received created distressing side effects. The toll it took on him was terrible to watch. I finally came to the point where I promised Maven that I would give him no more medication.

We tried different foods. We tried behavioral strategies. Nothing worked. Maven lost his appetite and huge amounts of weight, becoming a shadow of his former regal self. He became very anxious and cried incessantly. I became so obsessed with his health and his care that I hardly had a minute of time for the other two cats.

Instead of following me around the house, Maven began to hide, something he'd never done before. One day when I was searching for him, I found him crouched under my bed. Our gazes locked, and I could see his suffering. "Help me," his eyes pleaded. But there was nothing I could do to relieve his distress.

When Russ and I finally admitted to ourselves that our cat was living in agony, we made the decision to euthanize him. He was ten years old at the time.

My grief over the loss of Maven was terrible. I missed his presence in the home, the feel of his luxurious fur. It seemed that every advertisement for cat products on TV involved a fluffy white blue-eyed cat, which always reminded me of my loss. Russ and my children grieved as well. To help us all get closure, we held a memorial service for our departed kitty.

Now, I had only two cats to care for. I was hoping for at least a short reprieve from health crises. But immediately after Maven's death, Ziggy, who was sixteen at the time, began to show signs of physical decline and feline dementia. She grew very thin, and her hips became so arthritic that settling into a lying down position made her cry out in pain. She lost her bearings with the litterbox. Her demented soul-piercing howls kept Russ and I awake at night.

So, I was thrown back into the routine of countless trips to the veterinary clinic. Indomitable kitty that she was, Ziggy hobbled along in a state of deplorable health for two years. She became so ravaged by kidney disease that she looked like a fur-covered skeleton. Daily episodes of projectile vomiting caused her rickety old body to fall over from the exertion. Her suffering was heart-wrenching to watch.

But Ziggy didn't seem to lose the will to live. Unlike Maven, she didn't hide. She kept company with the rest of the family. She greeted us every morning with expectancy in her eyes, as if hoping the new day would be better for her than the previous day. It was always worse. Russ and I finally decided it was time to ease her out of her misery and into kitty heaven.

Ziggy never had been anyone's favorite, or the center of anyone's attention. In the company of her royal pedigreed peers, she'd been a sturdy little peasant, plodding along year after year. But in the vet's office, just before she received the injection that ended her suffering, I shared an incredible moment with her. As I held her in my arms, all the love that had never been expressed between the two of us came rushing forward, and for a few minutes, Ziggy was the love of my life. It was a beautiful way to let her go.

Now, we had only one cat. I was surprised that Leo was the last one standing, as in his early years, he'd been the most fragile of the three cats. He'd had health crises on a regular basis, one of which carried him perilously close to the brink of death.

Leo had played a heroic role in our lives, as he'd served as the glue that held Russ and I together during difficult years of our marriage. I knew that if my husband and I ever filed for divorce, we'd surely have a fierce custody battle over Leo. We often said to each other, "I can't imagine this house without Leo in it."

We wanted him to last forever. In fact, toward the end of his life, I wrote the following limerick:

Old Leo's on life number seven.
May his multiple lives reach eleven.
May it be a long while
Till he walks his last mile
To the place that we call kitty heaven.

But multiple lives notwithstanding, we had to face the fact that Leo wasn't immortal. He began showing signs of physical decline shortly before Ziggy's death.

Once again, I resumed the routine of trips to the veterinary clinic with a sick animal in tow. Leo was diagnosed with a heart problem and an incurable sinus infection that made it difficult for him to breathe. Several times when his breathing problem escalated to crisis proportions, we made emergency trips to the vet for shots to ward off his death. At one such visit, the doctor said to us, "I can't fix this," letting us know that Leo never would be healthy again.

Yet, she worked with us to give our beloved cat every chance at a longer life. We tried different medication regimens at home. We gave him shots. We forced pills down his throat, a procedure he fought tooth and nail. Every morning turned into a battle over getting him to take his medication. Russ and I often wondered whether we were doing the right thing by putting Leo through the torture. But we simply weren't ready to let go of the little guy who'd warmed both of our hearts for thirteen years.

Leo's difficulty with breathing made it hard for him to eat. Like the two cats before him, he grew very thin. He showed mental changes as well, losing the essence of who he'd always been.

While going through the heart-wrenching routine of caring for my third dying cat, a decision began to formulate in my mind. *I can't do this again,* I told myself. *I'm losing the stamina to provide this kind of intensive care. The veterinary bills are taking a toll on our finances. I don't have it in me to watch another pet suffer, or to cope with another loss. My years of being a cat mama are coming to an end. It's time to move on to another chapter of my life.*

I thought about other things I wanted to do with my time and energy, things that were incompatible with having a pet in the home. Having indoor cats made it hard to keep my house as clean as I wanted to keep it. I also wanted to add some décor that I knew cats would never leave alone. When I talked with Russ about my decision to end my role as cat mama, he readily agreed with me.

In late January 2016, it became clear that Leo was days away from death. I called the vet to discuss his condition. She informed me that Leo's suffering would increase toward the end, and suggested that we proceed with euthanizing him.

So, we said goodbye to our beloved pet and let him go. Russ and I immediately rid the house of all our cat food, toys, and supplies, so that we would not be faced with constant reminders of Leo.

Even though I had been preparing myself for Leo's passing, my grief hit me harder than I ever imagined it would. Leo's companionship had helped me make it through the long, lonely evenings while my husband was at work. I was at a complete loss without having my little darling on my lap. For the first few days after his death, I was unable make it through the evening without falling apart.

I desperately longed to see a cat, hear a cat, hold a cat. So, to temporarily assuage my grief, I went to a local pet supply store that had an adjoining shelter filled with cats available for adoption. I had no intention of adopting another cat. I just needed a kitty fix.

The first time I walked into that shelter, I became an addict. Day after day, I returned to get another fix. My grief-addled brain refused to face reality, making me look at all the cats through magical eyes. The shelter became a fantasy world that I couldn't stay away from. There were enchanted creatures everywhere, all calling from their hearts to mine, offering to save me from my distress.

Two particular cats enraptured me with their beauty. One was a petite female tabby with coloring and markings uncannily like those of Leo. I found her so gorgeous and so charming that I ignored the name posted on her cage and called her Marlena, after the movie star Marlene Dietrich.

The other object of my attention was a robust orange cat, scarcely more than a kitten. He'd had one ear clipped by a vet when he was neutered as a stray, which gave him a rakish look. I thought his thick, exquisitely patterned coat was the most amazing one I'd ever seen. He was aptly named Rusty.

I was aware that I wasn't thinking straight when I started fantasizing about bringing Rusty and Marlena into my home. I told my husband I was falling in love with them, but that I knew I shouldn't adopt them. "Stop me," I begged him.

After visiting the shelter to check them out himself, Russ agreed that Marlena and Rusty were splendid kitties. Rather than stopping me, he encouraged me to go ahead and arrange for their adoption.

At that point, something inside me screamed, *Wait! You are not ready for this. This is just your grief expressing itself. This isn't what you really want.*

But I had become weirdly possessive of Rusty and Marlena. In my mind, they were obviously so special that someone else was bound to snatch them up if I didn't act quickly to claim them as mine.

So, I began moving forward with the process of adoption. All the while, the voice of caution inside me screamed at the top of its lungs. I became extremely agitated, torn between my fantasy world and my own good sense. After filling out an adoption application one afternoon, I sat in the parking lot of my medical exercise program, overcome with panic, trying to breathe and center myself before going inside to exercise. *This isn't right,* my inner voice insisted. *This isn't what you really want. You need to speak up and stop this process before it goes too far.*

Still, I went ahead and made phone calls to the rescue organizations that were sponsoring Rusty and Marlena. And I learned that if you even make eye contact with those noble souls who work in the animal rescue business, they'll have a new pet in your home before you can blink twice.

In my agitated state of mind, I engaged in a great deal of confusing conversation with the rescue organizations. I thought I was just asking for information. They thought I was committing to adopting the cats I was inquiring about.

On a Saturday evening about two weeks after Leo died, I received a phone call from a worker in the cat shelter at the pet store. One of the animal rescue people had assumed that I'd already taken Marlena home with me. She had brought in another rescue cat to take her place, and wanted to know why Marlena was still there.

I did not explain to the caller that I hadn't yet made up my mind about adopting Marlena. Instead, I decided that the universe was telling me Marlena was meant to be mine. Russ and I immediately jumped into the car and drove to the shelter to pick her up. Having gotten rid of all our previous cat supplies, we had to make an emergency trip around the pet store to purchase what we needed.

When we brought Marlena into the house, she quickly claimed it as her own. Russ and I watched in amusement as she toured every inch of her new residence. First, she walked around the perimeter of our entire first floor. She insisted on checking out the view from every window. Then she proceeded to explore the upstairs and the basement as well. We could see that she wasn't a bit timid.

By every indication, it seemed as if Marlena was intended to be our cat. Duty overcame my inner reservations. Watching her through magical eyes, I found her ravishingly beautiful. We immediately took pictures of her and emailed them to my children, introducing them to their new feline sister. Having previously informed them that I was giving up my role of cat mama, I joked with them about the weakness of my resolve.

The following afternoon, we received a phone call from the organization sponsoring Rusty, telling us they were bringing him to our home. I went along with the plan, feeling powerless to protest.

Rusty's response to our house was completely different than that of Marlena. The poor fellow was terrified, and immediately ran for cover behind the couch. When we'd coax him out of one hiding place, he'd run to find another. Eventually, he found his way to the basement, which he deemed to be safe, and claimed that as his home. He refused to come upstairs, so we took food, litterboxes, and toys to the basement.

As the weeks passed, I did my best to settle into a new routine of cat care. I continued to look at my new pets through magical eyes, trying to deny the fact that I had engaged in an act of self-betrayal. But my inner voice would not keep quiet. *This isn't what you really want,* it insisted. *These creatures are sweet and lovely, but they are not meant to be yours.*

I thought about the commitment I'd made to these animals, one that could last for the next ten to fifteen years of my life. It terrified me.

While Marlena adjusted easily to her surroundings, we discovered that she had an unfortunate habit of biting without provocation. I became concerned for the safety of houseguests.

Within several days of being in our home, she developed an infection in one eye. *Oh my God,* I wailed inwardly, *I have another sick cat on my hands. I don't have it in me to deal with this again.* But I mustered the energy to pack Marlena in the cat carrier and drive her to the vet, the clinic I'd hoped not to see for a very long time.

While at the clinic, I encountered the doctor who had provided care for Leo in his last months. She hugged me, praising me profusely for being such a good cat mama, telling me that I'd given Leo more chances for a long and happy life than most people would have given him. The receptionist told me that Marlena was lucky to be in my home. I took their comments as reassurance that I had made the right choice in taking in Rusty and Marlena.

Perhaps this is one contribution I can make to the planet, I told myself. *I'm good at caring for animals. Maybe taking in strays is my calling at this point in my life.*

For the next ten days, Russ and I carried out a twice-daily routine of administering medication to Marlena's infected eye. It cleared up nicely.

After about a week in his basement home, Rusty began venturing up to the main floor for a few moments at a time before getting scared and flying down the stairs again. Every day, Russ and I worked on calming his fears, offering him affection, getting him to trust us, and coaxing him to explore other parts of the house.

We both discovered that the process of offering Rusty such intensive care resulted in the formation of a deep bond with the little fellow. Although Marlena was the cat whose appearance reminded me of Leo, Rusty resembled Leo behaviorally. He seemed to be on his way to becoming Leo Jr. When he finally came upstairs and joined family life, his growing attachment to us was deeply touching.

But there was something else going on in the house all this time. During Rusty's stay in the basement, Marlena often went down to keep him company. The two of them jumped on table tops and shelves, knocking over everything in sight, breaking one object after another.

They continued this behavior when Rusty moved upstairs. Particularly because of Rusty's highly active kitten ways and his propensity to tear around the house at top speed, my clean home was suddenly covered with a layer of cat hair. Litter was kicked all over the place. I swept and swept, but couldn't keep the mess under control. I tried to make the best of things, but every day, my heart sank a little lower.

Looking back, I suspect that during all the years I'd kept pets in my home, I'd had a slight cat allergy, showing up as mild asthma. But my allergic reaction to Rusty and Marlena was more than mild. Any time either of the cats came near me, I had difficulty breathing. I developed a severe, unrelenting cough.

As the weeks passed, the conditions in my home grew worse and worse. Cat dander was everywhere, and the quality of the air was terrible for me. But because of the commitment I'd made after giving up Miranda decades earlier, I did my best to hang in with my new pets.

Russ and I bathed the cats several times, trying to wash off the funk from animal shelters. We wiped their coats with a product formulated to cut down on cat dander. We bought new filters for our air purifiers and turn them on full blast.

But it began to feel as if my home had been invaded. I had lost my comfortable, serene environment. I was coughing violently, incessantly. While the cats ran freely and happily throughout the house, my only way of coping was to enclose myself in my bedroom with an air purifier. I got sicker and sicker. Emotionally, I spiraled down into a very dark place.

Lying awake one night, I made myself face what was happening to me. I'd taken two rescue cats into my home, but now it was time to rescue myself. I had to make myself a priority.

The next morning, I said to Russ, "I can't live like this anymore."

He understood. Sick at heart, we called the rescue organizations, informing them that we needed to return the cats. The woman from Rusty's organization expressed dismay, saying, "It's such a shame. You've been such a good home for him." Her words plunged a knife into my heart.

We packed up both cats and all their supplies and returned them to the shelter at the pet store. I leaned against Russ's shoulder and cried like a baby, both from the loss of the cats and from my sense of failure as a cat mama. I felt as if I'd betrayed the cats, particularly Rusty. I had worked so hard at getting him to feel safe, only to deprive him of the home to which he'd finally adjusted.

For the next few days, I was so shaken up and off-balance that I was the one knocking things over and breaking them.

I knew full well that I had brought all this trauma upon myself by neglecting to listen to my inner voice. Even though providing a home for a stray animal might be a noble thing to do, it was not right for me at that point in time. In an effort to circumvent my grief over Leo's death, I had tried to extend a role that had passed its expiration date. Additionally, I had allowed outside forces to influence me in making choices that were not in my best interest.

Now, I not only had to grieve the death of Leo, I had to deal with the loss of Rusty and Marlena as well.

This was one time when I insisted to myself that I HAD to learn from my mistake. Piling loss upon loss was so painful that I knew I never wanted to repeat such an experience. It was imperative that I start listening more closely when my inner voice cautioned me.

Furthermore, I recognized the danger of making decisions when emotionally distraught. I saw how unwise it had been to make a major commitment while in the throes of grief.

After thoroughly cleaning the house and getting treatment for my asthmatic cough, I began to feel much healthier, both physically and emotionally. I was able to turn my thoughts back to Leo, to come to terms with his death and to say a proper goodbye to him in my heart.

As I worked on restoring order to the basement, I felt the need to do something to commemorate Rusty and Marlena's brief stay in my home. So, I purchased a straw floral arrangement, something they undoubtedly would have enjoyed destroying, and set it on a table in the space where they used to hang out. I think of them every time I see it.

I struggled with the urge to check on Rusty and Marlena at the cat shelter, to ensure myself that they were okay in the aftermath of my abandoning them. But I knew that doing so would only set me back emotionally, and Russ made me promise to stay away from the shelter. A month passed before I finally felt strong enough to revisit the place that had once seemed like a fairytale world to me.

When I entered the shelter, I encountered no enchanted creatures. Only cats. They were sweet and beautiful, but none of them bewitched me.

I looked for Rusty, but he was nowhere to be found. I hoped that meant someone else had adopted him. I didn't want to entertain the idea that he might have been carted off to another shelter.

When a tabby cat got up from her nap and headed toward the food dish, I initially didn't recognize her as Marlena. I peered closely at her. It was undeniably my former pet. But the magic was gone. My realistic eyes saw her as just a cat like all the others in the shelter. She shot me a glance before burying her head in the food dish, but I saw no recognition in her eyes. The brief bond I'd shared with her was gone.

Weeks later, when I visited the shelter a second time,

Marlena was no longer there. I truly hope that both animals are happy and well-adjusted in new homes.

Shortly after Rusty and Marlena left our home, Russ and I found ourselves turning our attention to the creatures living outside our house. The transition from indoor to outdoor pets seemed to be a natural evolution. We both had animal-sized holes in our hearts that were soon filled by various species of birds, large and small, along with squirrels, chipmunks, rabbits, and the occasional raccoon. Russ set up birdfeeders and established a routine of putting out seeds and nuts for the animals on the ground.

We now enjoy animals without suffering from allergies, coping with messes in the house, or taking on the emotional pain and financial strain of caring for sick pets.

We supply the animals with nutrition, while they in turn provide us with unending entertainment. Russ has tamed the squirrels to the point where they will scramble for the peanuts he tosses them, much like our cats used to scramble for treats. He talks to the chipmunks as if they are his little buddies. The animals are so comfortable living in the trees and bushes in our backyard that I'm sure they've staked a claim on our property. If they could speak, they'd surely give our street address as theirs.

Russ has trained the animals to properly eat their seeds out of shallow bowls that all the species share, although the smaller creatures refuse to give up the uncouth habit of standing in their food dishes.

The lesson I learned from my unwise decision about cats was one I knew I'd never forget. It etched a deep impression in my mind.

A year later, during my post-cat redecorating efforts, I decided to buy a new area rug for our living room. Russ and I looked in many stores and on the internet. When viewing a rug in a store or online, it is hard to envision how it will look in your house. I ended up ordering and returning three rugs that didn't meet my expectations.

The process daunted me. Each time I made a less-than-satisfying purchase, I was tempted to give up and make do with it. But I listened when my inner voice said, *No! This isn't the rug you want. You don't really like it. It will bother you every time you look at it.*

So, I went through the repeated hassle of returning a rejected rug, then setting out on my search again. Thankfully, my fourth purchase turned out to be exactly what I wanted. Every time I step into my living room, I am glad I persisted.

I've also learned that making a series of decisions in rapid succession is too much for my brain to handle. In late January and early February 2017, I was dealing with buying the area rug and ordering glasses. At the same time, I was making decisions about creating a marketing ad for one of my books and settling on a cover design for another book. The weight of all those decisions plunged me into mental turmoil.

I hope the recent lessons I've learned will ease the strain of the remainder of my life journey. I know I need to avoid making too many weighty decisions at one time. I know not to make decisions when I am upset, exhausted, or in a state of confusion. I have learned to slow down the decision-making process, taking as much time as I need. Most importantly, I have committed myself to listening carefully to my inner voice of wisdom.

UNSPOKEN WORDS

Living with a brain injury has threatened to draw me into a deep well of silence. It is tempting to give in to that pull, to stay in that quiet space wrapped in my protective bubble.

Nature has endowed me with a personality on the quiet side. I've always had a tendency toward introversion. Prior to my injury, people would often say to me, "You need to speak up more. You need to be more outgoing."

I tried to follow that advice. I often told myself that I would be a more successful person if I was more extraverted, and from time to time, I would set a goal to become more outgoing. But those endeavors always seemed to run counter to who I really was, and I'd grow weary from the efforts.

That isn't to say that I was not a well-spoken person. I made a living by talking with clients in therapy sessions. Throughout my career, I gave presentations and provided trainings in professional venues. I occasionally did public speaking in other settings.

So, when I was referred to speech therapy a few weeks after sustaining my brain injury, I was flabbergasted. I'd never before had a problem with articulating my thoughts. However, my words were now buried deep inside me. I struggled to find them and bring them out. I'd lose my place in a conversation, forgetting what I was trying to say. Such difficulties led to a profound loss of confidence in my conversational abilities, from which I have not fully recovered.

Furthermore, speaking exhausted me. During my early speech therapy sessions, a ten-minute verbal exchange with my therapist was all I could manage. Then one day, we pushed our conversation to thirty minutes. My brain power suddenly sputtered and died, leaving me in such a state of mental anguish that uttering one more word seemed like more than I could bear. My speech therapist recognized my plight and quickly ended our session.

Seven years later, I can speak fluently, but only under certain conditions. Lengthy conversations still exhaust me. When I'm tired or experiencing brain strain, or when I'm tackling some difficult subject, it seems as if some internal speech mechanism is moving in slow motion. Every word comes with great effort. It feels as if I am slogging my way through a rugged terrain.

Most of the time, I simply can't think of anything to say to other people in social settings. When I notice my disinclination to talk, I remember a psychotherapy client I had years ago. Veronica was typically an energetic, talkative woman who was so entertaining that she often kept me laughing throughout the therapy session.

Then tragedy struck. Veronica had a heart attack, followed by open-heart surgery. Her lengthy recovery curtailed her normal work and social activities, and she spent many hours at home alone. During this time, the pace and volume of her speech in therapy sessions was reduced to a fraction of what it previously had been. She'd talk hesitantly for a few minutes. Then she'd look at me plaintively and say, "I can't think of anything else to tell you."

In the years since my injury, I've often identified with Veronica. I live a very quiet life, spending most of my time alone. Not a lot happens to me that I deem to be worthy of repeating in a conversation. In social settings, finding something to say often seems to require more energy than I am able to muster.

Listening to other people in a conversation can exhaust me just as much as speaking. When I discovered this new reality after my injury, I was dismayed. I'd spent thousands of hours listening to clients throughout the course of my career.

I had, in fact, developed a great deal of listening fortitude. I had listened to people who rattled on so fast that I could barely follow what they were saying. I'd sat patiently with people who didn't want to talk at all. I had engaged in "meetings of the mind" with people whose thoughts were disordered. I had listened to clients who pushed the bounds of civility, some who verbally attacked me. I had maintained unbroken listening in aversive environments: with clients who neglected their personal hygiene, in homes overrun by filth, in the presence of menacing animals.

However, despite my long history of doing so as a therapist, I am now unable to listen to speech that I find offensive or disturbing. While I'd like to think I've become a more compassionate person since my injury, I've become less able to listen to people who annoy me or raise my hackles. I never would be able to tolerate the problem behavior of clients the way I did during my career.

I am not proud of being so thin-skinned. But I need to recognize and accept the fact that I am now a hypersensitive person. I've learned from painful experience that listening to things that upset me can result in terrible emotional consequences. It can send my mind reeling into dark places.

It seems as if empathic listening, a gift I once practiced so well, has been taken from me. However, I suspect my listening is now meant to go inward, to the whispering of my own spirit.

Since my injury, ordinary conversations have seemed extraordinarily loud and frenzied. What other people consider lively and enjoyable wears me out. I am aware of the fact that people talk the way they've always talked. The change is in me.

Sometimes, I can have a good time in group conversations, so long as it is a very small group. But when a conversation bounces rapidly among a large group of people, that pattern triggers confusion in my brain and quickly exhausts me. It can take me hours, if not an entire day, to regain my mental balance after an experience like that.

During the years I attended my writers group, the number of people present varied greatly. When just three or four of us sat around the table discussing our work, I generally came away from the meeting with minimal distress.

However, the group was usually larger than that. When eight or nine people were squeezed around our small table, I'd begin to suffer from the highly energized conversation. Inevitably, I'd shut down and give up any effort to talk. At the end of the evening, I'd go home feeling painfully overstimulated.

For several years, I attended a very small Tai Chi class held in a spacious studio. That venue was perfect for me. Then, the studio was sold, and our class joined another class in a different venue. The class was now three or four times the size of what it formerly had been. The new room was far more crowded, and the volume of talking among group members increased dramatically.

Under those new conditions, the quality of my Tai Chi experience diminished greatly. I came home week after week feeling out-of-sorts. One day, I recognized what had happened to make me feel terrible by the end of the hour. Not wanting to appear quiet and withdrawn, I had attempted to interact with others around me. In the process of tracking the rapid-paced conversation, looking for openings in which I could interject something, I had exhausted and strained my brain.

After that, and many other similarly painful experiences, I decided to give up the effort to pace with others in highly animated conversations. In such circumstances, I now remain silent until the conversation dies down, or until someone turns to me and asks for my input.

My favorite group is my book club that meets on Monday mornings at my church. The friendships in that gathering are important to me, and I usually enjoy the content of our conversations. But there are times when the conversation and laughter become loud, or when several conversations are going on simultaneously. Those moments throw me into a daze. At such times, I sit quietly, my eyes closed behind my dark glasses, breathing deeply to get through my distress.

About two-thirds of the time, I come home from this group with my heart warmed by friendship. One-third of the time, I come home feeling dazed and exhausted from an unusually lively gathering. But I have determined that the benefits that accrue from the loving interaction outweigh the deep exhaustion that comes from too much talk and laughter.

When I'm out in public, such as in a store, a bank, or the post office, I am usually struggling to hold myself together as I negotiate whatever task I am trying to accomplish. I tend to shut down verbally. I imagine that I look to others as if I'm completely closed off.

Several years ago, I was shopping for a Christmas gift in a small store in downtown Saint Joseph. The owner of the store was friendly and helpful. I could tell that she enjoyed getting to know her customers, and that she loved sharing stories about life in the community.

Most customers would have enjoyed chatting with this pleasant woman. But I was already tired from trying to find what I needed in the unfamiliar store, and it took every ounce of my concentration to hang in with our lengthy conversation. I drove home feeling as if my brain had been battered by her words.

Half a year later, I stood at the checkout counter of a department store, worn out from my shopping excursion. The bubbly clerk was chatting with anyone and everyone around her. Suddenly, I realized that she was talking to me, and that I had been standing there like a statue, completely unresponsive to her verbal overtures. I forced myself to say a few words to her, then grabbed my purchase and fled the store.

Since my words now come with greater effort, I am more keenly aware of the value and weight of each word I speak. I attempt to express my thoughts in a few well-chosen words rather than exhausting myself with superfluous rambling.

Hearing my own negative words can traumatize me. Often, when provocative words are on the tip of my tongue, I asked myself, "Do I really want to deal with the painful consequences of saying this?"

As my social conversations are now infrequent, they are more precious to me. It pains me to see others taking conversations for granted, behaving thoughtlessly in their verbal interactions. I cringe when I hear people interrupting one another and talking over the top of each other.

One Sunday at church, I spotted a woman I knew I'd seen in another setting. I thought perhaps she'd been in my Tai Chi class. Coaching myself to break out of my bubble of silence, I approached her.

"I know I've seen you somewhere else," I told her. "Do you attend the Tai Chi class at the library?"

Her face lit up. "Yes, I do. I thought you looked familiar, and I was trying to figure out where I'd seen you before."

We exchanged a few more pleasantries. I was feeling inordinately proud of myself for having the courage to reach out to another person.

"What is your name?" I asked.

"Grace," she replied.

About that time, another woman, Lisa, came over to talk with Grace. I could sense her agitation as she impatiently waited to step in and claim Grace's full attention.

"And what is your name?" Grace asked me.

Before I had the time to speak my own name, Lisa blurted out, "Lois." Then she verbally elbowed me aside, taking over the conversation with Grace.

I walked away feeling deflated, wondering at Lisa's rudeness. Had she thought I was talking too slowly? Had she thought she didn't have time to wait around while I spoke my own name? Had she thought I was so disabled that I couldn't speak up for myself? The incident shook my confidence.

As I thought about what happened, I realized how a person with a profound disability feels when other people jump in to speak for them. How important it is for anyone to have the opportunity to express themselves, even if a speech impediment slows down the rate of their speech. Even if a medical condition renders their speech garbled and barely intelligible. Even if they can't speak at all and need to use a device to communicate. Certainly, every human being deserves the dignity of announcing their own name.

I haven't yet mustered the desire to strike up a conversation with the woman who so rudely interrupted Grace and me. However, I am grateful for the insight that humiliating incident taught me. I am now more aware of the pain of anyone who feels he or she never has a voice in social interactions.

While I've given up my efforts to become an extravert, I find that venturing a few words can sometimes open a door, breaking my feeling of isolation. At the gym where I am currently a member, I generally do my exercise routine ensconced in perfect silence, saying nothing more than, "Excuse me," if I've gotten into someone's way.

However, one day in June 2017, I encountered the gym owner on crutches, with a boot on one injured foot. Instead of letting the moment pass wordlessly, I emerged from my bubble of silence long enough to say, "What happened to your foot?"

Then I listened for a minute as he talked about breaking his ankle in a soccer game, and how he hated being forced to curtail his activity level. Since that interchange, he and I have greeted each other with a bit more warmth.

When I worked as a therapist, I had the privilege of engaging in deep conversations with people, getting to know them on an emotionally intimate level. Looking back, I see what a gift that was to me, and how that kind of interaction fed my soul.

Now, I miss the intimacy that comes from sharing thoughts with others. I long to know and be known on a deep level. But at this point in my life, I am consigned to being quieter than I've ever been before.

While I guard against letting the silence consume me, I enjoy resting there much of the time. To be sure, silence can be lonely. But in some ways, it also feels like a luxury. I've come to realize that, when the spoken word is set aside, there are treasures in the quiet places.

SOUL SISTERS

My husband and I moved to St. Joseph in 2006. While I met many new people during my first few years in Michigan, those new relationships might best be described as friendly acquaintances. I failed to develop any close friendships. I was very busy with professional pursuits and endless remodeling tasks in our new home. Lack of close friends was a concern, but was not at the top of my worry list.

After my injury in 2010, I was precipitously cut off from work and most of my social activities. Spending long hours at home alone made me keenly aware of my limited support system. I felt the need for a close friend who would love and understand me as I struggled to find my way through a very dark phase of my life journey. As I was unable to be out in public for any length of time, I wanted someone willing to sit with me in my quiet home and share quiet conversations.

In the early weeks after my injury, my Episcopal priest came to my house to visit as often as she could. Soon, she assigned Donna, a priest-in-training, to make weekly visits.

At that time, most people's personalities would have been too intense for me to deal with in my fragile state. They would have had to dial themselves down to a low setting to effectively relate to me. Donna was a thoughtful, soft-spoken woman who instinctively slowed down her conversation to respect the condition I was in. I never felt stressed by her quiet presence.

Sadly, this arrangement lasted for only a few months, as Donna completed her training and took on the responsibilities of her own parish. Because she needed to focus on her new employment, our weekly visits ended.

So, I looked around to see if I could find any other candidate for a close friendship. First, I set my sights on Kelly. She was someone I'd met at a group I'd attended prior to my injury. I was convinced that Kelly and I had a lot in common, as we'd had similar careers and shared similar interests.

I began issuing invitations to Kelly to get together and talk, even to meditate together. We had a few good times, and I enjoyed her company. But I noticed that she was not reciprocating by issuing any invitations to me.

Kelly was a highly energetic, free-spirited woman busy with her work, her travels, and her ongoing studies. It seemed as if she was always breathlessly on the run. She had difficulty carving out time for me in her schedule, and often canceled commitments we'd made to get together. Like a butterfly, she alighted in my life rarely and unpredictably.

When I finally realized that Kelly was not as interested in a friendship with me as I was with her, I felt deeply hurt. I shared my wounded feelings with my husband, who pointed out that Kelly never had been a good candidate for the type of friendship I wanted. As I had been before my injury, Kelly was a woman in the prime of her career and her studies. She was not looking to take on a close friendship with someone consigned to a slowed-down lifestyle.

Next, I turned to Sharon. Years earlier, she and I had been in a study group together. We'd had some interesting conversations, but had never developed a close relationship, as our lives had taken us in different directions. But half a year after my injury, she showed up in my life again, attempting to restart the study group.

Sharon seemed to be steady person who lived a quieter lifestyle than Kelly did. When it looked as if our paths were converging again, I took it as a sign that our friendship was about to blossom. I even sent her an email, expressing my happiness that we now had the opportunity to become closer.

Curiously, Sharon did not respond to that email. In general, her responses to my friendly overtures were sporadic. I learned that she was going through some tough personal problems. In an attempt to forge a bond with her, I offered to be there for her in her difficulties, hoping she'd want to be there for me as well.

But a friendship with me was simply not on Sharon's radar screen. I stopped bothering her, and she made no efforts to contact me. Our lives separated again when she moved out of the community.

During my brief association with Kelly, she had introduced me to Amelia, a woman who'd just come through a bout of cancer. Amelia had been expected to die from her illness, but had miraculously pulled through. As we'd both been through life-altering health crises, she and I immediately developed a deep understanding of each other.

Amelia had been a meditation teacher prior to her catastrophic illness. When I first met her, her health was beginning to stabilize, and she wanted to get back into her teaching.

I eagerly supported Amelia's desire to lead a small meditation group in my home. I enjoyed almost a year of friendship with her. She and I had long, riveting talks. My brain would grow so weary from our conversations that my body would shake from the strain. But I'd persist, as our discussions were so important to me.

Amelia knew what it was like for me to have my lifestyle destroyed by a catastrophic event. She knew my struggle to rise up again and find new ways to plug back into meaningful activity. She seemed to understand perfectly where I was in my physical, emotional, and spiritual journey. I thought I'd found a lifelong friend.

But Amelia truly had her heart set on resuming a career as a meditation teacher. The months of leading the group in my home were only a practice time for her, an opportunity to immerse herself in the work again. The day came when she announced that she was ready to pursue paid employment. Abruptly, she discontinued her leadership of the group in my home.

After Amelia left, I tried to maintain contact with her. She did not reciprocate my efforts to keep the friendship going. She was farther along in the recovery process than I was, ready to live a fuller life. She had her eyes set on the road ahead, and I was now in her rearview mirror. Sadly, I released my grasp on the friendship and let it go.

Looking back, I can see that Amelia appeared in my life at a critical juncture, helping me come to terms with the changes that my brain injury had thrust upon me. I am deeply grateful for her impact on my life. But our association was not meant to be a lasting one.

My final attempt at orchestrating a close friendship was with Jill, the only member of the meditation group remaining after Amelia left. She and I seemed to have an uncanny connection with each other. After Amelia's departure, I suggested to Jill that we continue to meet to support each other on our spiritual journeys.

The two of us did enjoy some wonderful times together, and for several years, her friendship alleviated my loneliness. But, to my disappointment, we were not the kindred spirits I'd imagined us to be. In terms of temperament, personal histories, lifestyles, and worldviews, Jill and I were polar opposites. We struggled to understand each other, and an underlying tension simmered in our relationship.

Early on, Jill confided that she'd grown up with a mother who'd suffered from chronic illness. This had put a damper on her childhood, inhibiting the freedom she'd wanted to enjoy. She told me that since then, she'd shied away from forming relationships with people who suffered from health problems, as she couldn't bear the thought of taking on such baggage again.

I wondered whether Jill was indirectly telling me that, because of my brain injury, she did not want to be my friend. Looking back, I see that I immediately should have clarified the matter with her, ending our association if that was what she'd wanted. But I pushed on with the relationship, all the while believing that, because of my impairments, I was not what Jill wanted in a friend.

During the next few years, I not only had the brain injury to contend with, I also went through back surgery, eye surgery, asthma, and several nasty bouts of poison ivy. Each time I faced a health problem, I imagined that Jill took it as a personal affront.

I wanted to talk about my struggles, but any time I mentioned a health issue, I received a cool reception from Jill. I sensed her determination not to get involved with the problems of someone who reminded her of her ailing mother.

I became guarded in our conversations, side-stepping issues I thought would upset Jill. Choosing topics of conversation seemed like picking my way through a minefield.

Instead of acknowledging our differences, even our incompatibility as close friends, I became obsessed with trying to fix the relationship. I worked overtime in trying to understand Jill. I tried hard to explain who I was and where I was coming from, never sensing that my words were resonating with her. I tried to please her, to be acceptable to her, to fit with her. I denied my own beliefs in order to embrace hers. Looking back, I see that I created a fantasy relationship with Jill, projecting onto her the qualities I wanted a friend to possess.

I suspect that, all along, I was not picking up on Jill's sweetly worded hints that she wanted to discontinue our meetings.

Whenever I'd stop issuing invitations to get together, there would be an echoing silence on Jill's end of the conversation. I'd wait for a while, then reach out to her again, and we'd resume our association. This pattern repeated itself several times before I completely let go, allowing the friendship to breathe its final breath. I suspect Jill was relieved to have me out of her life.

When I walked away from that friendship for the last time, I recalled a dream a client had recounted to me years earlier. Heather, who was part Native American, was struggling to ward off an ex-husband who manipulated her emotionally and kept her in a state of chaos and confusion.

In her dream, Heather was listening to the sound of Native American drums, which she knew represented the drumbeat that guided her life. A voice in the dream warned her that if she continued to allow her ex-husband to keep her under his control, she no longer would be able to hear the beat of her own drum. The dream had a sobering effect on Heather, strengthening her resolve to shut out her ex-husband's manipulation and move forward with what was right for her.

After letting go of my relationship with Jill, I understood the significance of my client's dream in a new way. I'd become so caught up with my efforts to fix the friendship that I'd lost the sound of my own drumbeat. I had been trying to march to Jill's beat, which wasn't right for me. This ended up leaving me feeling emotionally battered, confused, and lost. It took me weeks to find the rhythm of my own life again.

Pain shadowed me for a long time after this last friendship failure. I had no confidence to reach out to anyone else. Months later, when my wounded feelings had healed enough so that I could see things in perspective, I felt foolish about everything I'd done in my efforts to make friends. I had tried to insert myself into the lives of people who had no room for me. I had tried to forge friendships with people who weren't in the market for another relationship, and then had expected them to provide the support that I'd wanted from them. I took a good look at myself and saw that I had become the personification of emotional neediness.

I realized that if I indeed was going to enjoy close friendships in my new community, those relationships would need to form naturally. I saw how my trying too hard had resulted in nothing but pain. I told myself that I could still be open to people without overextending myself, that I could still relate to others while staying solidly in my own personal space.

I also had to accept the fact that having people come and go in my life was a normal experience. That some people were meant to be my lifelong friends, while others were destined to be in my life for a few years or a few months. And that some would be present with me for only a moment.

One day at my gym, I noticed an elderly man walking on a treadmill. He was wearing a pair of bright red gym shoes, a pop of color in his otherwise subdued appearance. When I encountered him as I was leaving the gym, I stopped to comment on his shoes.

"Those are some snazzy sneakers," I said. "Do they help you go faster on the treadmill?"

His eyes lit up, and he shook his head in woeful humor. "I've been getting a lot of ribbing about these shoes recently," he said. "The only thing they do is get me in trouble. They don't do anything for me on the machine."

Then, as I headed out the door, he said, "You have a nice day now." I returned his kind wishes.

I've never encountered the red-sneakered gentleman since then. Our friendship lasted only for a minute. But that minute lifted both of our spirits, and I'm sure that each of us had a better day than we otherwise would have had.

One day as I contemplated my failed quest for a close friend in my local community, a thought came to me: *When it comes to friendship, quality is more important than quantity.*

I looked at what I already had, what I've actually had for a very long time: two friends who both live hundreds of miles away from me, but who are unfailingly there for me. Both of these soul sisters are as reliable as the sunrise in my life.

I've known Roseanne since I was in first grade. We went through elementary, middle, and high school together. As adults, we've maintained contact through letter-writing and phone calls.

Marcia and I met in graduate school, and have maintained our friendship since then. Our correspondence through letters has evolved into the exchange of weekly emails.

Both of these dear women responded to my brain injury the way trusted friends do in such a crisis. Emotionally, they moved closer to me. Their support of me has never wavered. They have made efforts to understand my challenges, and I never fear that they will abandon me. Both are my friends for life. We've pledged that to each other.

As I thought about these friendships, I suddenly understood a truth that pertains to anything we have. Asking for more creates a feeling of deprivation. Being thankful for what we have cultivates inner peace. So, I shifted my thoughts to focusing on how grateful I am to have two beautiful soul sisters in my life.

I decided to shower these friendships with more love and attention. As the years have passed, my soul sisters and I have turned friendship into an art form. In addition to them being there for me, I make every attempt to be a faithful friend to them, to support them through their life trials.

In an email to Marcia in May 2017, I wrote, "I wish we lived closer so we could sit and chat and share a cup of tea."

About a week later, I received a package in the mail containing a variety of teabags from Marcia's personal stash. The enclosed note said, "Here is some tea to connect us together. Enjoy and think of our friendship."

Even if I never develop closer relationships in my current community, I still have a world of treasure in my friendships with Roseanne and Marcia. I tell them often what they mean to me.

While I take comfort in my close friendships, socializing in general remains a challenge for me. Because I know that I will encounter a great deal of sensory stimulation in social settings, I approach social gatherings with a great deal of trepidation. Sometimes, I come away from an event thinking, *Well, that wasn't so bad.* Other times, the stimulation is so unbearable that I vow never to return to such a gathering. Because it can take several days to recover from a massively stimulating event, I've developed a fear of what might happen each time I venture out to socialize.

Avoiding excessive stimulation while guarding against the danger of falling into isolation is a constant struggle for me. My spirit is warmed by interacting with others. My brain doesn't like it at all, and nudges me toward the life of a recluse. I am constantly on the lookout for social settings where I can enjoy heartfelt interaction with others in an atmosphere that is quiet enough to suit my brain and nervous system.

Over the years, I've gotten better at analyzing the conditions surrounding a potential social event, taking into consideration the lighting and the likely level of noise and commotion. I can more accurately predict which events I can tolerate and which are likely to be overwhelming.

Years ago, I had a dream in which I was trapped in the middle of a large, noisy, chaotic group. I had no means of escape, and I felt miserable. But a voice in the dream directed me to find an inner place of stillness in the midst of all that commotion. When I find myself in that type of environment in real life, I try to follow the advice given in my dream.

With my diminished ability to socialize, small experiences of closeness mean more to me. The exchange of an affectionate touch or a few kind words can make my day.

At my church, saying the Lord's Prayer is part of the weekly liturgy. During that prayer, many people reach out to hold the hand of the person sitting next to them. As I am usually alone in a pew, I rarely have a hand to hold.

One Sunday several years ago, when it came time to recite the Lord's Prayer, I was standing behind an elderly man. With great effort, he turned to face me, tap-tapping with his cane to support himself as he maneuvered his ailing body in a half-circle. Smiling broadly, he extended his hand to me. Holding that gnarled hand was one of the best experiences I've ever had with saying the Lord's Prayer. I vowed to be the one to extend my hand the next time.

In my Tai Chi class, we have a closing ritual that involves standing in a circle and holding hands. When I am feeling especially deprived of human warmth, I savor that moment, noticing how the other hands feel in mine. Some are plump and soft, some are thick and strong, some are small and thin. Some feel warm, while others are cool. The connection always feels good.

Since my injury, I have been surprised by how well-meaning but insensitive people respond to my condition. I'm quite sure others with disabilities experience the same thing.

About a year ago, I shared some information about my brain injury with a few people in a small social gathering. Their responses shocked me. Some of the people glibly commented on others they'd known with brain injuries, describing their bizarre symptoms. One woman staggered around to demonstrate how her aunt had moved after her injury.

Then they began to outdo each other by spouting out what they'd heard or read about brain injuries. I stood there feeling hurt and humiliated while my injury was exploited as a topic of a lighthearted and entertaining conversation.

I wondered if the same people would have stood around the wheelchair of a military veteran with a missing limb, chatting about all the amputees they'd ever known. "I had an uncle whose leg got blown off in the war." "My neighbor lost his arm in a farm accident." I hoped they never would do such a thing.

In contrast to the insensitive remarks, a woman at the gathering, along with her son, approached me and spoke to me privately in quiet tones. They expressed appreciation for the information I'd shared, acknowledging what a difficult experience the injury has been for me. The son spoke with just as much sensitivity as his mother did, and I wondered what she'd done to cultivate such an admirable trait in him.

I have difficulty knowing what to do with loud and aggressive people in social situations. I shy away from them, as I feel bowled over by their intensity. But while I have difficulty tolerating conversations with them, I try to guard against completely shutting them out of my life.

Recently, I met a new person whom I had admired from a distance. I had, in fact, looked forward to making her acquaintance. I was disappointed when I discovered how overbearing she was in personal interactions. Being around her wore me out, and my brain began making notes about avoiding her in the future.

But my heart whispered something else: "Wait and see. Even though you don't enjoy talking with her, she might serve some other purpose in your life. Don't write her off. You might appreciate something about her someday." And that, in fact, has turned out to be true.

However, my social caution serves me well in other ways. In the past, my naïve, unsuspecting, be-nice-to-everyone nature led me to open the door to people who ended up doing me harm. The results of being so unguarded were devastating.

I know full well that I no longer can afford to allow dangerous people to enter my life. Such experiences were difficult to bounce back from prior to my injury. Now, I might never be able to recover from them.

Because the amount of time I spend in social interaction has diminished since my injury, my confidence has waned. I constantly do battle with social anxiety, feeling insecure about how I measure up to those around me. *Am I speaking well enough?* I wonder. *Is my appearance okay? Does my brain injury make me come across as weird?* I tend to see myself as the only vulnerable person in a room full of people who are striding confidently through life.

One day, while feeling alone and insecure at the supermarket, I coached myself to look carefully at all the people around me. I saw a steady stream of imperfect individuals whom I suspected were struggling with one challenge or another: chronic illness, job problems, financial setbacks, family crises, relationship failures, legal trouble. Problems not seen at a superficial glance. Problems I would never know about.

In that moment, I was reminded of something I've always known, that to be human is to be vulnerable. People are just people, with all their flaws and insecurities. And I am just one of them.

ON THE FRINGES

In late 2013, I watched a television series called *Breaking Faith*, a show about youth from the Fundamentalist Church of Jesus Christ of Latter-Day Saints (FLDS) who were trying to escape their highly controlled and restricted lifestyle.

The stories of their struggles riveted me, hitting my heart dead center. I understood the difficulties those young men and women encountered in trying to break free and assimilate into mainstream society. No matter how hard they tried to fit in, they never fully succeeded.

I wished I could help those FLDS youth, to reassure them, to ease their fears. But I knew they were not easily helped. All of them had to find their own way, in their own timing.

I know what it feels like to be marginalized, to live on the fringes of mainstream society. I come from a predominately Mennonite and Amish lineage. Both of my parents were raised in large Mennonite communities in northern Indiana, where their German and Swiss ancestors had settled. A few years after they married, they moved to southern Indiana, where they founded a Mennonite mission station in decidedly un-Mennonite territory.

Thus, while my parents grew up surrounded by a sizable community of faith, I grew up as a member of a minority population. The lifestyle dictated by our small church contrasted sharply with the way of life of the people living around us. We Mennonites looked different. We behaved differently. We weren't allowed to participate in activities that the rest of the community enjoyed. I felt like a misfit, an oddity.

I spent my adult life trying to prove that I was normal, that I could fit in. But I never fully succeeded. The memory of those early dissimilarities lived as a knot of pain deep inside me, leaving me to feel permanently set apart from those around me.

After sustaining a traumatic brain injury, I once again occupy a marginalized position in society. Again, limitations have been imposed upon me. My childhood restrictions involved such things as, "You can't cut your hair or wear slacks. You can't go to dances or to the movies." My new restrictions are, "You can't hold down a job. You can't go everywhere you want to go in the community. You can't tolerate activities that most people handle with ease."

As a child, I felt pain when I couldn't watch the TV shows other children chatted about, or when I couldn't wear the style of clothing other little girls wore. Now, I feel pain when others talk about the latest books they've read, the hobbies they enjoy, the places they've traveled.

Something about this feels full circle. I started out life feeling like an oddity. I once again feel cut off from mainstream activity. Perhaps I am meant to learn something from living a marginalized lifestyle.

Not only did I see myself on the fringes of society growing up, I also felt marginalized in my own family. I was the seventh of nine children born to my mother and father. Our beleaguered family was stressed by overcrowded living quarters, inadequate finances, and my parents' overwhelming responsibilities with the mission station they had founded.

My overworked parents had no time for dealing with childish nonsense. Thus, my growing up felt rushed, and I had little support in dealing with the developmental challenges of childhood. From a very early age, I determined that I was on my own, that my survival was up to me. I had to hang on for dear life. If I lost my grip and fell off the wagon, I would suffer the fate of the American folklore character Pecos Bill. No one would notice I was missing, and the family would trundle on without me.

As one of the younger children, I felt like I was in the way, an aggravating little brat unworthy of the space I took up in our crowded house. I saw myself as someone to be shoved aside so that the more important people in the family could carry on with their lives. My very existence seemed to create unhappiness for my mother and siblings.

Early on, I concluded that I was the worst member of the family. If my parents' children would have been ranked in order of desirability, I undoubtedly would have come in last. I developed a belief that I was inherently bad, and that there was nothing I could do to change that unfortunate reality. It wasn't so much about how I behaved. It was about who I was.

I remember one unhappy day when I was nine or ten years old. After a row with my mother, I soberly took stock of my personal resources. By that time, I'd already noticed that some people earned a favorable standing in life by being good-looking, by being especially nice, or by having a charming personality. And some people just seemed to have an indefinable quality that elicited love from others.

I knew none of that was going to work for me. *I am ugly,* I told myself. *I am bad. I have a rotten personality. No one will ever love me.*

That left me with only one ticket for successfully riding the train of life. I had to be smart. That was the only way I was going to survive. So, from that day on, I sought to define myself as an intelligent and capable person. Constantly in the back of my mind was the never-articulated thought: *If I do well enough, if I achieve enough, I might finally pay off the debt I incurred by bringing my unwelcome presence to this planet.*

In my quest to prove my worth, I never could accept failure. I tried hard never to fall down on the job. My own weakness was something to be despised. Time and again, I pushed myself until I was on the verge of collapse.

In school, I could tolerate no grade lower than an A. Getting a B on a test or an assignment shook me to the core. It made me feel as if my identity was dying.

Because I believed that I was an inherently bad person, that the essence of me was poison, I shied away from getting close to others. I didn't want anyone to come near enough to see my badness, or to be contaminated by my toxicity.

When I started massage therapy training in the mid-1990s, I had to confront this painful belief about my poisonous essence. One day, I broke down and cried, confiding to my instructor my fear of transmitting my toxic energy to the clients I touched. I wanted to help people, not harm them. Discovering that I could soothe people with my touch came as a wonderful surprise.

After decades of this never-ending quest to prove myself, there came the fateful day when being hit by a car left me lying unconscious in the middle of the road. It didn't take me long to realize that I never would fully recover my former self, and that being smart and capable never would form my identity again. In the early days after the accident, I looked at my injured face in the mirror and said to myself, *I now need to be a person who does the best she can with what she has left.*

Even though part of me still wants to hang on to my old identity, my brain injury gives me the opportunity to explore a different idea about who I am. At the end of my life, when I will be unable to do even as much as I do now, it will be more important than ever to have a different understanding of my identity: something deep and fundamental and inherently worthy, something that has nothing to do with being beautiful, charming, smart, or talented.

I have never thought of myself as being an interesting person, although at different points in my life I tried hard to cultivate that image. While I've harbored a self-concept of being bad and unworthy, most of those outside my family have held a different opinion of me. They see me as an overly serious, goal-oriented person who focuses on responsibility while others take time to enjoy their lives. I have never been the life of the party. I've never been one to captivate a group with my humor or my colorful stories. I doubt that anyone has ever viewed me as the intriguing, free-spirited character I've often longed to be.

I know what it's like, in a group setting, to watch people's gazes sweep past me, only to see their faces light up when they spot someone more exciting.

This has always torn at my heart. But now, I experience this phenomenon more often. As conversation is tiring for me, I have little to offer in a group setting. I've sometimes thought that my quest for a local best friend was unsuccessful because the people I tried to befriend didn't find me interesting enough.

Once, when I suffered hurt feelings by reaching out to someone who didn't reciprocate my efforts, my husband offered me a different point of view. "I've known this woman for years," he told me. "She's never been interested in anyone else. She's only interested in her own opinions."

That may seem like an unflattering thing to say about another person. But my husband's perspective was helpful to me, rescuing my self-esteem for at least a few minutes. *Perhaps the fault doesn't lie in me for not being more interesting,* I mused. *Perhaps the failure of my friendship with this woman is because of her inability to show interest in others.* It struck me that showing interest in another person is an investment that can reap many benefits.

However, while I've often longed for others to be interested in me, I've never been comfortable with being in the spotlight for too long. Being the focus of attention has always frightened me.

As a child, I determined that being unseen was the best way to stay safe in my family. If I remained outside my strict, ever-vigilant mother's line of vision, and if I steered clear of my teasing siblings, then I could avoid being hurt.

As I grew older, I continued to believe that being unseen would allow me to avoid the judgment and criticism of others. On an unforgettable day in one of my graduate school classes, my professor was about to hand back papers we students had written. I had been confused about the assignment, and was unsure whether the structure and focus of my paper was on target with what he'd expected. I was sure he was about to place in my hands a paper marked up with red ink, topped off with a deplorable grade.

Because I wanted no one to witness the humiliation I was about to experience, I did something I'd never done in class before. I kept my heavy winter coat on. I needed an extra layer of protection against judgment and criticism. If the worst happened, the coat could swallow me up, protecting me from the probing eyes of others. So, I huddled under that coat, sucking myself in, trying to make myself small.

As it turned out, my suffering was for nothing. I got an A on the assignment.

Years later when I was practicing psychotherapy, I noticed an interesting pattern among the children I treated. Whenever I met child clients for the first time, they would be understandably nervous. In encouraging them to feel at home with me, I would invite them to take off their coats or jackets. They always refused. And I always knew why. They needed an extra layer of protection in the strange new environment of the therapist's office.

As much as I haven't wanted to expose my weaknesses and inadequacies to others, I have, in the years since my injury, opened myself up by sharing myself through writing. I struggle mightily with this. The scared child inside me warns me that it is a colossal error to be so vulnerable as to offer the essence of me to the world. Thus, writing and selling books seems dangerous and wrong, the violation of an important rule that I've honored for so long.

Yet, I believe it is important for me to overcome the wound inflicted during my childhood, the wound that resulted in my seeking privacy as a way of staying safe. Mustering the courage to share myself may be one of the most important things I can do in my remaining time on this planet. Something inside me demands self-expression.

My workers at Michigan Rehabilitation Services have urged me to be bold about announcing who I am as a writer, behavior which is alien to my quiet nature.

Perhaps there is a middle ground between hiding myself and shouting boldly to the world. On New Year's Eve 2015, I recorded an important thought in my journal. I was, at the time, feeling stuck in my work with MRS on the task of marketing my books. I wrote, "I do not need to strive or push. I can expect my work to flow without exhausting myself with counterproductive efforts. I do not need to move into the world shouting and clamoring for attention. I can speak softly from my heart. Those who are meant to hear, will hear what I say."

While being unnoticed can feel safe, it is also undeniably painful. Feeling invisible has sometimes made me feel dead inside. Having attention and feedback from others helps us sustain our sense of self. After my brain injury, when I became quieter and less socially active, I began seeing myself as less than a full person.

If you approach me, I often think, *I won't have a lot to offer you. And you will be disappointed.*

Because of my diminished sense of importance in social settings, I find myself reluctant to introduce myself to others, or even to wear a nametag in group situations. One day, my husband and I went to a local bookstore to inquire about arranging a book signing. He had to give me a nudge forward, whispering, "You need to introduce yourself." It hadn't occurred to me to do so.

One cold winter Sunday morning in 2017, I awoke several hours before dawn. For me, those early hours can be either a special time of connecting with the divine or a time of destructive brooding. That morning, I fell into dark thoughts about being an invisible and unimportant person, unworthy of occupying the space I take up on this planet.

Recognizing that my thoughts had wandered off into harmful territory, I asked God to help me get a better perspective on the matter.

I was hoping to hear a still, small voice in my mind whispering words of wisdom. But perhaps because of my tendency to be overly serious, the universe decided to teach me a lesson through a bit of humor.

When I entered my church later that morning, I was still in a mindset of being invisible and unimportant. I slipped into a pew, imagining that no one even knew I was there.

It so happened that the Episcopal bishop of the Western Michigan Diocese was scheduled to speak at our church that morning. Being a relative newcomer to the Episcopal Church, I am not fully acquainted with its structure and traditions. I had never met the bishop.

I watched in awe as he paraded up to the front of the church, looking formidable in his long white robe and ornate hat. However, when he opened his mouth to speak, I discovered that this bishop was a funny guy. His homily, peppered with humor, jolted me out of my dark rumination, making me sit up and pay attention.

A part of our church's liturgy is Exchanging the Peace, a time when congregants greet one another with a handshake. During the exchange of peace that Sunday, the bishop made his way through the crowd, greeting one person after another.

When he came to me, he said, "Thanks for laughing at me. I needed that." And without missing a beat, he moved on to shake the hand of the person behind me.

Bewildered, I returned to my seat, wondering at the bishop's strange words. I realized that I must have been smiling broadly throughout his homily. I thought about what he must have seen as he looked out over the audience. Even though I'd imagined myself to be invisible, I had been directly in his line of vision, sitting there with my oversized dark glasses and a big cheesy grin on my face. It startled me to think that I had not been unseen after all.

I had to wonder about the myriad little roles we all play in the universal plan. Maybe the only thing we need to do is to show up somewhere and allow the divine choreographer to do the rest of the work. Perhaps I had been meant to sit in that particular pew, wearing my bug-eyed sunglasses, grinning like a Cheshire cat, meeting the bishop's need to be appreciated for his humor.

Whatever the significance, the weird little exchange made my day, and I went home laughing.

It occurs to me that there is a major flaw in my theory that invisibility means safety. I got hit by a car precisely because the driver didn't see me. But sometimes, being unseen truly poses an advantage.

Throughout my school years, I was a front-of-the-class type of student. Looking back, I am embarrassed to think about how obnoxious I was. In my never-ending quest for perfect grades, I didn't want to miss out on anything that was being taught. I was constantly raising my hand to ask or answer questions.

However, there was another reason for my front-of-the-class, teacher-ingratiating behavior. Being a preacher's daughter, my parents instilled in me the importance of setting a good example for my peers. I knew I would face severe consequences if I failed to live up to those expectations.

So, I sat up front in my classroom, maintained good behavior, and diligently applied myself to my schoolwork. Of course, this never won me any popularity points with my fellow students. They saw me as a teacher's pet and a Goody Two-Shoes.

When I started Tai Chi classes in 2012, a year and a half after sustaining my injury, I felt nervous and inadequate, as did the rest of the newcomers in my class. The other inexperienced students sought out spots in the back of the room so that their errors would not be on display. As always, I found a spot in the front, so that I could more easily follow the teacher's instructions.

Four years later, our small class moved to a different location, joining with another class that quadrupled the size of our group. I continued to claim my spot in the front of the room. As I was now considered to be an experienced student, newer students sometimes told me they were following my lead.

Having others' eyes on me made me decidedly uncomfortable, as I knew full well that I could never get through the hour without making numerous mistakes. Furthermore, I didn't feel I had the strength to carry the responsibility of being a role model in the class. My enthusiasm for Tai Chi waned.

Years earlier, I'd been given a piece of advice about what to do when feeling stuck in life. I was told that doing one small thing differently in my daily routine could give me a new perspective. It could be something as simple as sitting in a different chair at my dining room table, which would allow me a different view of the room.

I decided to apply that advice to my Tai Chi class. One day, I abandoned my front-row spot and claimed a spot in the very back of the room. The place where, during my school years, all the screw-ups and troublemakers sat.

Immediately, I felt a weight roll off my shoulders. Now, I could participate in class entirely for my own benefit, rather than carrying the burden of leading others in the right direction. In the back row, I found that I could sink more deeply into my own experience. I could be in my own space, doing my own thing, even if I was a bit out of sync with the rest of the class. No eyes were on me. I felt no need to impress anyone, or to please the teacher. If I made an error, I didn't have to worry about letting anyone else down. I started looking forward to the class again.

I took a bit of pleasure in my secret rebellion, feeling a kinship with all of the back-of-the-room students I'd ever known in school, the snickering, note-passing, paper-wad-throwing crowd. I saw their perspective from the back of the classroom, and understood why they'd made the choice to sit there.

Now, the back of the room is my favorite place to be. Occupying that spot takes less out of me, and I feel less exhausted at the end of the class.

Since my injury, I have, in many ways, stepped off the stage and out of whatever spotlight I've ever occupied in my life, into the ranks of the seldom heard and seldom noticed. I often feel sad about this.

But every loss comes with lessons. Perhaps I need to learn something about life from the profoundly humbling experience of living with a brain injury. To learn what it is like, not to excel, but to function below average. To understand what it feels like to be slow, to trail behind the pack, to come in last.

Perhaps everyone who feels like a winner in life should have at least one opportunity to gain perspective through such an experience.

Recently, when brooding over feeling like a misfit, it occurred to me that all of us seek to assuage our loneliness by associating ourselves with some social, cultural, or religious group. While this meets a need for identity, the boundaries that we draw around our groups serve to shut others out.

So, whenever I am unable to find a comfortable niche where I can claim belonging, I remember that, ultimately, my identity is as a member of the human race. That I share this identity with every person that I encounter. That I am just as connected to someone who lives halfway around the world as I am to the person living next door to me. And perhaps my true identity goes even deeper than that, to being a citizen of the universe.

INSIDE THE BOX

Decades ago, when I first heard the phrase "thinking outside the box," I thought the concept was brilliant. It fit a philosophy of life I'd already adopted. I never wanted to be limited by conventional expectations of me. I wanted to believe there were possibilities for my life of which I couldn't conceive. I routinely stretched my boundaries, stepping outside my comfort zone to accomplish things I never thought I could do.

As I come from a conservative background that was reluctant to allow women the same range of opportunities afforded to men, earning a graduate degree and embarking upon a professional career involved implementing a decidedly outside-the-box plan.

When I started graduate school in the summer of 1985, I was living with my first husband and our three children in Goshen, Indiana. My master's program was in Indianapolis, a three-hour drive away. For the first twelve weeks, I was required to be on campus Monday through Friday. So, I rented a tiny efficiency apartment where I stayed during the week. On weekends, I went back home to be with my family.

This was an outside-the-box venture that was almost more than I could handle. I missed my family terribly during the week. I knew no one in Indianapolis, and was dreadfully lonely. I repeatedly got lost driving in the city. I cried every day, before class and after class. Probably even during class.

Throughout the fall and winter months, I continued my commute to Indianapolis, staying in the city for two or three days at a time. One night, I foolishly drove down to the campus in a blinding snowstorm, in a car with a dying battery. When my car stalled at an intersection, I couldn't get it started again. In the days before everyone carried lifesaving cell phones, I sat stranded and helpless in my car as the bitter cold seeped into my bones. I suddenly had a sense of what it would be like to freeze to death.

Thankfully, I was rescued by a kindly couple. After they jumpstarted my battery, I followed them to a place where I could get a new battery installed. Then I continued my treacherous journey. When I got to where I was staying for the night, I soaked in a bathtub of hot water, trying in vain to bring my body back to its normal temperature. Burrowing into a bed piled high with covers failed to warm me up. It took all night to get that icy feeling out of my bones.

But I made it through my graduate program, crawling across the finish line battered and bedraggled.

Over the next twenty years, I continued to push the boundaries of what I thought was possible. Growing up, dancing had been off-limits for me. As a child and teenager, I had enviously watched others dancing, their bodies moving gracefully and skillfully. I had felt awkward and stodgy in comparison. So, after I completed graduate school, I spent a decade taking dance lessons of various kinds, trying to prove to myself and to the world that I had a graceful side to my personality.

While still employed as a clinical social worker, I ventured into a secondary career as a massage therapist. My training involved three years of long commutes between my home in Goshen and my school in Kalamazoo, Michigan. After that, I studied a form of energy healing called Healing Touch. Completing the requirements to become a Healing Touch Practitioner also involved lengthy drives across the country to various training venues.

In 2006, I received an invitation to travel in Europe with a friend. International travel might be commonplace for many people, but it never had been for me. I'd barely stepped across our country's north and south borders into Canada and Mexico. I'd never imagined that a trip to Europe would be in my future.

When I received the invitation, I had no money to fund such a trip. My first impulse was to decline. I had, in fact, declined a similar invitation from this friend ten years earlier.

Going to Europe is impossible for me, I told myself. But then, my stubborn determination kicked in, and I decided that nothing was going to stop me from turning such an outside-the-box fantasy into a reality. For a year, I stashed away every dollar I made from my secondary career as a massage therapist. By the summer of 2007, I had saved enough money for a ten-day, low-budget trip to England and France.

Unfortunately, the trip was not the delight I'd imagined it would be. I encountered one unforeseen problem after another,

143

and came home from this once-in-a-lifetime adventure feeling traumatized. Still, creating this opportunity for myself strengthened my belief in the validity of outside-the-box thinking.

After my brain injury, I stubbornly clung to the image of myself as a person who could venture outside her comfort zone. *If you try hard enough,* I'd tell myself, *if you push hard enough, you can make this happen.* But time after time, I was hit with a harsh new reality. Stretching my boundaries and testing the limits of my capabilities no longer worked for me. Pushing myself too hard invariably resulted in sensory overload, cognitive failure, emotional meltdowns, and extreme fatigue. I finally realized I needed to start thinking inside the box, to consider what activities were safe and reasonable for me.

Driving is one activity where inside-the-box thinking is imperative for me. Prior to my injury, I thought nothing of embarking on lengthy road trips, driving hundreds of miles on my own. But now, my vision challenges, coupled with my attention problem and my tendency to tire easily, make driving long distances dangerous for me.

My sister Rhonda lives in our childhood community of Beanblossom, Indiana, more than a four-hour drive from where I live in Michigan. In the past, I had driven down to see her many times. Several years after my injury, I received a call from her. She informed me that our sister Ellen, who lives in Arizona, was flying out to see her. The two of them wondered if I would be willing to drive down to Beanblossom so that we could all enjoy a weekend together.

I sadly informed Rhonda that I no longer was able to make that drive. She seemed surprised. I was afraid that she didn't believe me, that she thought I was making an excuse. But I knew full well that four hours on the road alone would spell disaster for me, especially on the busy bypass around Indianapolis where multiple lanes of traffic travel at high speed. Not only would I be risking my own safety, I would be endangering others as well.

During the months of my friendship with Amelia, I often fretted to her about the confinement my brain injury imposed upon me. I was deeply frustrated by the fact that I was having difficulty getting to former social activities: meetings at the ashram in Kalamazoo, Michigan, and my Siddha Yoga group in South Bend, Indiana. Both cities were more than an hour's drive from my home. I felt incomplete without these activities, and couldn't face the idea of letting them go.

But efforts to get to Kalamazoo and South Bend exhausted me. Once, I attempted to drive on my own to my Siddha Yoga group, and my brain flipped into a daze while I was driving through downtown South Bend. This put me in a compromised mental state in the middle of city traffic. The experience terrified me. When I finally arrived at the group, I couldn't enjoy the activity, as I was too worried about making it home safely.

One day, Amelia introduced me to a concept from an eastern religious tradition: *When a bird flies too high, it sings off-key. When it perches on a lower branch, it sings a sweeter song.*

Never in my life had I aspired to perch on a low branch. I'd always wanted to soar. But what Amelia said struck a deep chord in me. I knew that when I moved quietly and peacefully through my days, taking small steps forward, my internal song was sweet. Reaching too far or trying too hard to make things happen left me squawking and screeching.

Attempting to get to my former activities in Kalamazoo and South Bend was an example of me trying to fly too high. I finally realized it was time to utilize resources inside the box of my own community, the small town of Saint Joseph. I could drive to a location just a few minutes from my home, enjoying an activity while perched on a lower branch and singing a much sweeter song.

Sadly, I've discovered that I am no longer a good traveler, even when I am not behind the wheel of the car. In June 2014, my husband drove me down to Beanblossom for a two-day family reunion. This was the first time I'd spent the night away from home since sustaining my brain injury.

I made it through the first day of the reunion, but not without exhaustion. The second day, Russ and I had difficulty coordinating our schedules with other family members. We had agreed to meet my siblings for lunch in the little tourist town of

Nashville, where he and I had spent the night. After checking out of our hotel, we found ourselves with several hours to pass before our scheduled lunch meeting.

We walked up and down the streets of Nashville, wandering in and out of shops. In the process, I subjected myself to an overload of sensory stimulation. Suddenly, a dark, murky cloud descended on my brain, along with a feeling of confusion and mental suffering. I couldn't bear to stay another hour in town waiting for our lunch engagement. We called my sister Rhonda, leaving her a message that we were heading home because I was not feeling well. I felt terrible about leaving so abruptly, without saying a proper goodbye to family members.

Two years later, with that experience still haunting me, I declined to attend a second family reunion in Beanblossom. Perhaps if Russ and I put more thought into managing our schedule and our surroundings, a future reunion might be viable.

I underwent cataract surgery in December 2015. By the spring of 2016, my eyes were stabilized, I had the proper glasses, and warmer weather with longer daylight hours had finally arrived. Joyfully and optimistically, I resolved to venture out and reclaim my pre-injury independence. I committed myself to making monthly trips to Goshen, to visit my two sons and to attend a study group there. The route to my destination was uncomplicated, and did not involve driving in dangerous city traffic.

The first time I embarked upon the trip to Goshen, I felt euphoric. I was sure this was a new beginning for me, that I'd broken out of my brain injury confinement. I felt like my old self, a strong woman who could go anywhere she wanted to go.

However, I soon discovered that I'd planned an overly ambitious agenda for myself. After a seventy-minute drive followed by an hour-long visit with my sons, I was exhausted. I went to my study group with a depleted store of energy. By the end of the meeting, I was so fatigued that the drive home was difficult and dangerous. It took a full day to recover from the strain of the trip.

I made four or five more trips to Goshen that spring and summer. I kept thinking I'd adjust to this new routine, that it would become easier for me. Sadly, it never got better. My ability to tolerate the outing never improved, and I finally gave up the idea of making any more trips.

As our wedding anniversary approached in June 2016, my husband and I talked about how we wanted to celebrate. I told Russ I wanted to go to a zoo, something I hadn't done in more than twenty years. I thought for sure that strolling outdoors looking at animals would be an activity I could easily tolerate.

The zoo nearest our home is a small one in South Bend. As we planned our agenda for the outing, we decided we'd first take care of necessary business, getting my car serviced at a dealership in South Bend. Then we'd go to the zoo, and after that, we'd have a nice meal in a restaurant.

The weather was perfect that day, with a bright blue sky and temperatures in the seventies. I was so pleased that fate was smiling on our special day.

At the dealership, we had to wait much longer than we'd anticipated while my car was being serviced. I had difficulty sitting in the building with its insufferable artificial lighting. From time to time, I'd wander outside, but the sunlight, unfiltered by clouds, beat down on me with equal ferocity.

By the time we arrived at the zoo, I realized the perfect summer day was not the gift I'd thought it would be. I was wearing my wrap sunglasses, but they provided insufficient protection from the intensity of the midsummer sun. As we looked at the animals in their zoo habitat, the brutality of the solar assault ruined my enjoyment. Soon, my sole aim was to find patches of shade where I could escape the unbearable sunlight.

The last place we stopped at the zoo was an enclosed exhibit housing reptiles and nocturnal creatures. The building was dark and dank, and the smell of the animals was overpowering. The sudden change in the sensory environment completely undid me. I was hit with the same reaction I'd experienced during my weekend at the family union: a dark, murky feeling in my brain, accompanied by disorientation and mental agony.

After we exited the building, Russ and I immediately left the zoo. I was feeling too miserable to face the environment in a

147

restaurant. We decided to head back home to Saint Joseph, hoping the lengthy drive would give my brain enough time to recover so that we could enjoy a meal in our own town.

I did feel a little better by the time we reached the restaurant we'd chosen. Thankfully, we were able to sit in shaded outdoor seating, sparing me from exposure to the lighting and commotion inside the building. But I was still so disoriented that I could neither read nor comprehend the menu. Russ had to help me decide what to order.

I was terribly disappointed that the outing I'd so eagerly anticipated had turned out so poorly. Russ and I did a postmortem on the event. He suggested that combining the pleasurable outing with the business of getting my car serviced had not been the best idea, as waiting inside the dealership had exhausted me before we even arrived at the zoo. We determined that a shorter outing, rather than a full day's excursion, would be in my best interest. The obvious lesson, of course, was to bring along a wide-brimmed hat the next time I would be exposed to intense sunlight.

After our zoo outing, Russ and I successfully went on a few shorter outings, exploring new places and activities closer to our home. On Memorial Day weekend 2017, we drove thirty minutes to a neighboring town where we visited a flea market. Although taking in all the sights resulted in visual strain that caused gait problems for me, I did not completely fall apart as I'd done on our zoo trip. I was able to recover quickly, and we counted the excursion as a success.

I now understand that it is better to enjoy outings in small bites, rather than trying to ingest a feast.

On a Friday evening in July 2017, Russ and I traveled to Goshen, as I was scheduled to do a book signing in a bookstore there. I had anticipated this event for several months. I knew that handling the sensory stimulation would be challenging. I just hadn't wanted to imagine how difficult it was going to be.

It happened that my book signing coincided with another event in town, in which classic cars cruised up and down Main Street, right past the bookstore. The area was congested, as many people had set up lawn chairs on the sidewalk to watch the parade of old cars. Finding a parking spot was difficult, and getting to the bookstore meant slogging our way through crowds of people.

The bookstore was a quaint and charming establishment, an old building that had been refurbished for its new usage. The ancient wooden floor creaked with every step the customers took. Not only did the place sell books, it served as a hangout for local people. My husband commented on how fun it would be to work in a store like that, and I agreed. I thought about how much I would love to browse the endless aisles of books. Sadly, I had to acknowledge that my visual impairment no longer allowed me to enjoy that kind of activity.

The store was very busy that evening, with throngs of people streaming in and out. Within minutes of entering the store, my brain flipped into a dazed mode and remained there for the rest of our two-and-a-half hour stay.

The noise of the traffic outside, coupled with the din in the store, pounded relentlessly on my nerves. The old floor creaked incessantly. People milled around me on every side, making my skin crawl. And, of course, I had to deal with the lighting in the store.

I made every effort to speak normally with the people who approached my table to look at my books. Old friends stopped by for lengthy conversations. The effort to converse while dealing with an overwhelmingly stimulating environment placed an enormous strain on my brain.

On the drive home, my brain began to fall apart. The mental agony was unbearable. It felt as if something had exploded inside my head, leaving loose wires dangling dangerously, sparking and misfiring. I knew I never wanted to repeat such an experience.

The following day, my brain was still reeling from the beating it had taken the previous evening. I couldn't shake off the feeling that I was still under assault. Even the slightest sensory stimulation felt like too much for me. I desperately wanted to escape my body, as I couldn't bear the idea of continuing to live in the earth's harsh sensory environment. I felt like a fish pulled out of my watery habitat and thrown up on the shore. Or an artic creature transported to a tropical rainforest.

Or an alien from another planet unable to survive in Earth's atmosphere. I told myself I no longer belonged in this world.

In an effort to sooth my suffering brain, I went outdoors to putter in my gardens. And there in my flowerbeds, with a soft breeze blowing on my skin, I felt at home again. *This is a habitat in which I can survive,* I told myself. *This is one part of the planet where I can still thrive.*

I knew that inhabiting a noisy bookstore for more than a few minutes was no longer something I could manage to do. But I was grateful that the earth still offered me some environments where I could feel safe and comfortable.

I thought about all the other individuals living in this world who have difficulty with their environments, who are unable to comfortably inhabit public places. Not only those with brain injuries, but also those who suffer from severe allergies or compromised immune systems. I hope that all of them can find some comfortable space on this earth in which they can enjoy a full life.

I can list off countless times since my injury when I've suffered devastating consequences from pushing myself too far outside the box. Still, I fall into the trap of envisioning myself doing things I can no longer comfortably enjoy. *Yes!* I think when I hear about some new activity. *I can go there. I can do that. Wouldn't that be fun?* Or, *I SHOULD go there. I SHOULD do that.* Then reality hits, and I realize that such an experience would be far outside the range of what I can tolerate.

Russ and I have not been on a vacation trip since my injury. The farthest we've traveled is to my family reunion in Beanblossom. The idea of going on a longer trip is both enticing and daunting. Certainly, I know better than to attempt visiting a large city. We would need to go to a destination where we could spend time in the soothing environment of nature.

I experience grief every time I hear people talking about their travels. Shortly after my injury, a friend excitedly recounted to me the details of a vacation she'd just enjoyed in a distant state. She had no idea the impact her story would have on a person who, at that time, could barely tolerate a trip around the supermarket.

When I traveled in Europe ten years ago, I had a taste of an experience I was unable to fully enjoy because of all the aversive conditions I encountered. Since then, I've wanted to go back, taking Russ with me. I fantasize about how I'd do things differently the second time around.

I know my brain could never tolerate revisiting London or Paris. But I would love to return to the rural area of England around Stonehenge. I'd like to stay there for a week, revisiting that sacred monument, fully savoring that experience.

I've looked at this possibility from every angle. But I still can't conceive of how I could tolerate the eleven-hour flight to England, how I could negotiate the massively stimulating environment in a busy airport, how I could adjust to unfamiliar surroundings in a foreign country without overstressing my brain. If I am unable to handle two hours in a bookstore, how would I ever manage such a feat?

Still, my husband and I have discussed such a trip. We've identified things we could do to reduce my exposure to excessive stimulation. Perhaps someday, we will figure out how to make such an adventure possible.

But the trip is probably a pipedream. Being a writer and a storyteller, most of my adventures must now take place inside my mind. I can enjoy living vicariously through my characters, making them go wherever I want them to go.

Even though I'm perched on a low branch these days, I still need challenges. Otherwise, I would experience stagnation. I strive for a middle ground, somewhere between hiding in my protective cocoon and being plunged into a state of agitation and confusion.

Manageable challenges serve to perk me up. Working on new plantings in my gardens or creating a novel arrangement in a flowerpot can make my day, so long as I don't take on too big of a project. The same holds true for reorganizing or redecorating efforts in my home. Mastering a small challenge can boost my confidence, but taking on too great a challenge can set me back.

Several of the people who've worked with me at Michigan Rehabilitation Services have suggested that I speak at the brain injury conference in our state capital of Lansing. At first, the idea excited me. I recalled all the times I did public speaking during my career, and I envisioned myself doing so again. I saw giving a presentation on brain injury as a way of giving back to the community, of advocating for other brain-injured people, of making a difference in the world.

But then, I began to consider reality. I had not done any public speaking since my injury, not even in front of half a dozen people. I had no idea whether I would have the stamina to get through such a speech. What if my brain would go into a meltdown and I could no longer think clearly? What if I grew so exhausted from speaking that I would be unable to continue? How would I deal with the lighting, the noise, and the commotion without going into a daze? And how would I even get to such a conference? Driving that distance and trying to negotiate the traffic in a large, unfamiliar city would be completely out of the question for me.

What kind of toll would the pre-event anxiety take on me? And afterwards, how many days would it take for me to recover?

After thinking this through, I suggested to my workers that, before taking on such a challenge, I should first practice speaking to small, local groups of people. They agreed with my idea. But so far, no such opportunities have come my way.

During the hot summer months in Saint Joseph, I visit Lake Michigan less often than I do during the spring and fall. The hordes of people on the beach during swimming season trigger my anxiety, making it impossible for me to enjoy quiet contemplation of the magnificent scene. But once the weather begins to cool and the crowds on the beach have dwindled to only a handful of people, I tell myself, "Now it's my turn."

In September 2017, summer seemed to switch itself off immediately after Labor Day. On the same day that Hurricane Irma ravaged Florida, I made my first pilgrimage to Lake Michigan in several months. The temperature was pleasantly cool, the sky was cloudless, and the gentle waves splashed softly on the shore. As I gazed out over the placid lake, I felt very fortunate to enjoy such serenity while people in another part of the country were being terrorized by floodwater and destructive winds.

I had tucked a snack and a few essentials into the same bag I'd used on my trip to Europe ten years earlier. The bag brought back memories of my once-in-a-lifetime adventure, and I smiled as I reminisced about the places I'd gone and the iconic sights I'd seen. But that day, I was on another adventure, albeit a tiny one.

I thought about the overwhelming stress I'd experienced on that European trip. In contrast, my trip to one of our country's magnificent Great Lakes was stress-free, and I felt grateful that such a destination was within several blocks of my home.

A flock of seagulls lounged on the sandy beach, as if resting after the commotion of the tourist season. As I walked along the shore, the gulls in my path lethargically moved a few feet away from me. They did not fly away in fear, as they were accustomed to humans visiting their habitat.

I sat on a swing and ate my snack in the calming, rejuvenating environment, deciding that I most certainly needed to return to the lake in the very near future. The following evening, I packed a sandwich and a thermos of decaf coffee, along with old bread for the seagulls, and ate my dinner by the lake.

Once again, I found the seagulls resting in the sand, unperturbed by my presence. But the moment I threw out the first scrap of bread, all the gulls within a hundred feet of me roused from their lethargy. With shrill screeches and a mighty rush of wings, they flew to where I was sitting, just near enough to catch any morsel of food I tossed to them. Most of the bits of bread I threw out never had the chance to hit the ground, as, with graceful swoops, the gulls deftly snatched the morsels in mid-air.

In those few minutes of interaction, the birds felt like my personal friends. I felt less alone on the planet. I left the beach with a renewed sense of wellbeing, grateful that I still have a whole world of delightful, inside-the-box adventures to enjoy.

Even if pushing myself outside my comfort zone no longer works for me, I still hold to the idea that there are possibilities for the rest of my life of which I can't conceive. While my activity has been curtailed, my determination remains. I have resolved to do everything I can within the parameters allowed by my brain injury.

BACK TO THE PRESENT

In the early months after my injury, my eyes were so sensitive that watching television for any length of time was too much for me to bear. However, I soon discovered that watching shows in black and white was less taxing than watching shows in color. Thus, I ended up turning my attention to classic movies from the 1930s and 1940s.

At first, I watched those old movies because they were easy on my eyes. But I became obsessed with them because they were easy on my psyche.

With my altered sensory experience of the world, I felt disoriented in my physical surroundings. Furthermore, I was bewildered by the technology that was proliferating around me, new developments that I didn't have the cognitive ability to understand or the visual ability to use. I didn't feel at home in the world of the present.

As I watched the old black and white movies, I found myself sliding backward into the world of a bygone era. A world that moved at a slower pace. A world where radios, landline phones, and manual typewriters represented the highest level of technology. A world where people composed hand-written letters instead of communicating through text messages and social media. I didn't need to struggle to understand the social culture of that past era. The old movie world was unchanging. It never flooded me with bewildering new developments.

I became acquainted with all the movie stars of that era, taking pride in learning their names and something of their personal histories. I soon identified my favorite actors and actresses, mentally joining defunct fan clubs for deceased stars. These long-gone people became my contemporaries, my personal friends in my make-believe world. I became infatuated with certain male stars: Cary Grant, William Powell, Humphrey Bogart, Melvin Douglas. Dapper, slick-haired men in wide-lapelled suits and fedoras became attractive to me.

I can't exactly recall what finally booted me out of that nonthreatening world. Perhaps it was because I ran out of old movies to watch. But there came a day when I knew it was time to muster the courage to once again face life in the present.

It seemed as if I stepped into a time-travel machine and took a long, long trip back to the current era. Back to the fast-paced, confusing world where I wasn't sure I could find a place to belong. But I knew I had to take the chance.

While stuck in that bygone era of old movies, I frequently fell into brooding on the idea that my life was over. I was just biding my time, hiding out in my make-believe world until death finally came to rescue me from my state of half-existence. But a fragment of faith kept telling me that I still might have future chapters of my life to live. And that if I didn't drag myself out of the past and back into the present, I would miss living out the full extent of my purpose here on earth. I knew that staying stuck in the past would put a damper on my personal evolution, causing me to miss out on knowing future versions of myself.

In the first year and a half after my accident, I received occasional acupuncture treatments. Upon checking my pulses, my acupuncturist would inform me that my energy was very low. She would repeatedly tell me that I needed to protect myself from negativity, because I didn't have the strength to handle it. She advised me not to watch the news on television.

Her advice may have been valid. But it also became an excuse for me to keep my head buried in the sand, to deny the reality of what was going on in the world around me. For the next five years, I remained a superficial consumer of national and world news, taking in just enough to be marginally informed about current events.

Then came the controversial and unsettling presidential campaign of 2016, followed by the tumultuous era of the Trump presidency. I was so frightened by what was happening that I decided I needed to tune in and stay informed. I needed to see what was coming down the pike. I didn't want to be blindsided by some catastrophic event.

So, in a complete reversal of my former avoidant patterns, I became a news junkie. While I was unable to take in the news through reading, I educated myself on current issues through watching cable channels on TV. As I'd done with the long-dead movie stars, I came to know all the players in Washington, DC. I could identify by face and name the presidential staff, cabinet members, members of Congress, and members of the press.

Admittedly, I now watch too much news. Sometimes, I find myself becoming overly agitated, overwhelmed with feelings of doom. At times, I need to limit myself, to give myself a mental health break. But I remain convinced that staying well-informed is preferable to my old habit of keeping myself in the dark.

Refusing to part with an old car was another way I kept myself stuck in a past era. Most of my life, I've cared little about cars, requiring only that they be reliable sources of transportation. But in the late 1990s, the New Beetle came out on the market. I found that model so visually appealing that I fell in love with it, and was determined to get one for myself.

Never in my life had I purchased a new car on my own. I felt bold and empowered as I ordered a brand new, bright blue Beetle from a local dealership. Weeks later, when my Beetle arrived, I was inordinately proud.

From the beginning, my beloved car had lots of problems. When it was just a few years old, the power windows began to malfunction. Utilizing the drive-up window of a bank became problematic, as I never knew how my cantankerous driver's side window was going to behave. At times, I'd be forced to get out of the car to complete my transaction.

While my son Zane and I were on a road trip to visit my daughter, who lived in Pennsylvania at the time, the passenger window completely gave out, stuck in the down position. On the way home, Zane and I got caught in a blinding rainstorm with a wide-open window. My poor son got more than a little wet.

When Russ and I moved to Michigan in 2006, I discovered that the tiny Beetle wasn't suited for driving in a Michigan winter. Getting stuck in snowdrifts became a frustratingly routine experience.

Each year brought new repairs to my Beetle. We poured thousands of dollars into the car. Among other things, we had the catalytic converter replaced three times. No matter what repairs we made, the *check engine* light refused to go off. We never quite knew what was going wrong.

Once, the Beetle broke down on my way home from work.

Because I was unable to reach Russ by phone, I had to abandon the car in a parking lot and walk the remaining two miles home. As the repair bills mounted, Russ started telling me the car was not worth investing any more money in it.

But I loved that car. It felt like me. Other people said it suited my personality. I had an emotional attachment to the Beetle that I've never had to another inanimate object. I forgave it all its faults, and hung on to it for dear life every time Russ tried to talk me into getting rid of it.

Five years after my I sustained my brain injury, when the Beetle was sixteen years old, my husband finally put his foot down and refused to put any more money into repairs. By that time, the front bumper had fallen off, and Russ repeatedly had to wire it on so that I could manage to drive a few miles around town. He insisted that it wasn't safe for me to drive another winter in a vehicle that was breaking down in every conceivable way.

So, I finally relented, allowing my husband to buy me a Subaru, a vehicle well-equipped to handle Michigan snow. We traded in the Beetle, which the dealership deemed to be a heap of junk, giving us only five hundred dollars credit for it. Sadly, I said goodbye to my beloved blue bug, and we drove home in a silver Subaru Forrester.

The Subaru has been an excellent vehicle for me, performing very well in inclement weather. But I've never developed the deep attachment to it that I had for my Beetle. To me, the Subaru is just a car.

Letting go of the Beetle forced me into some deep reflection. I realized I had been hanging on to my broken-down car because it symbolized an era from my past: a time when I was an independent woman who could buy a cute little car of her own choosing, proudly paying for it with her own hard-earned money. In letting go of the Beetle, I had to let go of the past and move into the present. Like it or not, I am now a woman who drives a sturdy vehicle bought for her by her husband.

I've had to go through a similar process with clothing. My fashion style has changed over the years. Early on in my career, I wore spiffy suits with classy blouses, determined to identify myself as a professional woman. Over time, my taste in clothing shifted to a more bohemian look, which I decided suited me better.

After my injury, I wanted to hang on to certain signature garments, especially my bohemian skirts, which reminded me of a time when I was a stronger, more vibrant woman. I had to face reality when some of those garments started looking dated and worn-out.

Reluctantly, I've let go of items that no longer suit me, coaching myself to dress in a way that reflects the me of the present era. While I don't have a lot of money to spend on clothing, I have become adept at taking advantage of sales and coupons. Thus, I've kept my closet stocked with attractive clothing at little cost.

While I am far from the most fashionably dressed person in the world, keeping myself in clothing that looks relatively current is one way of keeping myself open to the present era of life on this planet.

Unlike my husband, I never have been a lover of technology and electronic devices. Russ often wants to buy me the latest technological gadget, insisting that it could make my life easier. He generally has difficulty talking me into the change, as I tell him my current way of doing things is just fine.

I use technology as a means to an end, learning whatever I need to learn in order to accomplish what I want to get done. Thus, I reluctantly push forward in my mastery of technology, with my husband as my ever-present coach.

I have a cell phone, but I use it infrequently. I rely on it only when I am away from home. As just a few moments of staring at the small screen is visually painful for me, I am unable to participate in our current eyes-on-the-phone lifestyle. I have never developed the habit of using the multiple functions on a smartphone. I do not engage in the ubiquitous practice of texting. I feel decidedly old-fashioned, as I remain dependent on our landline phone.

I do have a Facebook account, but I don't spend much time on it. I can scroll through posts for only a short time before I start feeling sick. When I budget my eye-power for the day, Facebook is allotted little of that precious time.

Because having sound piped directly into my ears overstimulates my nervous system, I don't listen to music through headphones. I remain stuck in the era of CDs.

However, if I need to read a book, I join the latest trend by using an electronic tablet. This allows me to increase the font to a size I can clearly see. It also allows me to change the setting to a white font on a black background, which eases the strain on my eyes by cutting down on the glare from the screen. I very rarely attempt to read anything from a traditional book.

For years, I have enjoyed the pastime of going on walks. I love taking in the nurture that the world of nature offers me. I've had countless times on my walks when a sight hit me in a way that lifted me into the realm of magic. I have stood transfixed, taking in the enchanted scene, wishing that fleeting moment could last forever.

Many times, I have retraced certain routes, hoping to relive a magical moment I'd previously experienced. Sadly, it never happens a second time.

One day when I set out in search of a magical moment from the past, I was struck by a thought: *By trying to cling to special experiences from the past, I miss the magic available to me in the present moment.*

I am becoming more acutely aware of when it is time to let something go: a car, an article of clothing, an activity, a moment of magic. Slowly, I am mustering the courage to face life in the present. I do not want to miss out on knowing who I am in the current era of my life, and who I will become in the future.

DELAYED RECEPTION

From 2003 to 2010, I was involved with both the Hindu ashram in Kalamazoo, Michigan, and my Siddha Yoga group in South Bend, Indiana. A prominent activity in these two groups was the chanting of Sanskrit mantras, beautiful melodic intonations capable of inducing trance-like states in the chanter. The Sanskrit words were powerful, imbued with meaning.

The spiritual leader of the Kalamazoo ashram once said this about the chanting: "When you chant the name of God, it's like depositing money into a bank account. Then, when you are old and sick, you can draw comfort from this account."

In other words, when I chanted those sacred mantras, I was giving myself a gift in the present, which I would not fully receive until much later.

I had always thought that when I retired from paid employment, I would have the freedom to study all kinds of subject matter I'd never had the time to explore while I was still in the workforce. I had envisioned myself taking classes, going to conferences and retreats, stuffing my brain full of information.

That, of course, is not how things turned out for me. I've grieved over that turn of fate.

But I've discovered that my loss has a silver lining. Since I am now unable to take in as much new information as I did in the past, I find myself drawing on what I've already taken it, knowledge that has lived inside me for years or decades. I now have the time for a deeper contemplation of that knowledge, to see it from new perspectives, to understand meanings that had previously eluded me.

It seems as if I am just now receiving gifts of knowledge and wisdom that were given to me a long time ago. Just now, my mind and heart are ready to open and embrace those gifts. Since I am no longer a ravenous consumer of information, I can savor the sweetness of what I've already taken in. I have ample time in my life and space in my mind to do this.

I often recall something I've read in the past, or wise words that someone spoke to me, and suddenly, the meaning is illuminated in a new way. Sometimes, I understand that everything I need to know is already there inside me, waiting to be called up to my awareness.

Growing up as the daughter of a Mennonite minister, I attended church three times a week: Sunday morning, Sunday evening, and mid-week prayer meeting. I found the services to be insufferably long and boring. Mercifully, the singing of hymns offered relief from the dry and dreary portions of the service.

As I child, I knew the lyrics to most of those hymns, but I paid them no attention. What I valued about the hymns were the tunes.

Strangely, in the past few years, old hymns from the remotest parts of my memory have been coming to the forefront, hymns I haven't sung or even thought about in decades. I am repeatedly surprised when I find myself singing one of those old songs in my head.

For the first time, I am actually hearing the lyrics of these hymns. The words amaze me. I get a sense of what the author was feeling at the time he or she penned the poetry, emotions akin to those I am experiencing several centuries later. I understand what he or she was trying to convey to the future singers of the hymn.

In a remarkably uncanny way, specific hymns pop up to address whatever is troubling me at the time. It seems as if a mechanism in my brain sorts those old lyrics into special files, labels them according to subject matter, and sends comforting phrases to my conscious mind whenever a need arises.

My quiet, contemplative post-injury life also affords me the opportunity to fully receive loving words and kind gestures that were given to me many years ago, gifts I had been too distracted or too defensive to appreciate at the time.

When I was in high school, I was not popular with the boys. I was labeled a "smart girl," which, in the eyes of my male peers, rendered me unsuitable for dating. Once, I overheard a popular male classmate giving sage advice to one of his friends. "You should never date a girl who is smarter than you," he intoned.

Then he noticed me standing nearby, and said, "Sorry about that, Lois."

I knew that in insinuating that I was too smart to get a date, my classmate didn't mean to be unkind. But his words hurt me deeply.

Perhaps I should say that I was never popular with the popular boys, none of whom showed the slightest interest in me. However, it seems that I did have several admirers among the quiet boys, the young men generally bypassed and discounted by girls looking for male attention.

During my junior year, a short, chubby, red-haired fellow named Ronnie Harris sat next to me in my chemistry class. He was a quiet, sweet-natured boy who remained outside the churning adolescent drama that permeated the hallways and classrooms of our school. Ronnie and I were friendly with each other, although not close friends. I never considered him to be boyfriend material. I assumed he never would have the confidence to ask me or any other girl on a date.

One day as we chatted before class started, he propped his elbow on his desk, leaned his plump cheek against his hand, and looked at me intently. "Lois," he said, his blue eyes twinkling in his round freckled face, "someday, I want to marry a woman like you."

I can't recall what I said to him in return. I do know that his words embarrassed me. At that point in my life, I was so emotionally guarded that I no ability to take in a compliment. So, I put Ronnie's sweet words out of my mind, and I rarely thought about him after that.

That is, not until one night in 2012, when I dreamt that I was attending a high school class reunion. In the dream, I was preoccupied with what several of my popular classmates were doing, and my gaze followed them as they walked out the door of the room.

Then, I spotted Ronnie Harris sitting there by the door. I hadn't even known he was at the reunion. His round face was luminous in the murky darkness of the dream. When we made eye contact, he smiled at me, sending me a beautiful, glowing beam of love. At the same time, an aura filled with magnificent colors flashed around his head. I gazed at him in awe.

When I awoke, I immediately knew what had happened. The words of admiration that Ronnie had offered when we were teenagers had, through that dream, finally reached me. His loving gift had been biding its time in the ethers, waiting until it could find lodging in my heart. I finally recognized how sincere Ronnie's words had been, and what a supreme compliment that adolescent boy had given me.

For days after the dream, my heart felt tender, warmed by words spoken so long ago. I had no idea where the adult Ronnie Harris lived, or what direction his life had taken. But in my mind, I thanked him for his gift.

During my junior year of high school, I also had two male friends named Calvin and Perry. I had secret crushes on both of them, but neither showed any interest in having me as a girlfriend. However, they both enjoyed teasing me.

One day, they approached me snickering, informing me that I had a secret admirer. I perked up at the news, until they revealed the identity of the boy who was in love with me. It was Jerry Slater. I recoiled in horror.

In my snooty teenage mind, I thought of Jerry Slater as a caricature, the archetypal dork, the weirdest of the weirdos. While he was an intelligent fellow, he was socially inept and decidedly unattractive, with thick glasses, an overbite, and an odd gait.

"You guys are lying," I shot back at Calvin and Perry. "Jerry Slater doesn't love me."

"It's true," they insisted, laughing at my consternation.

Day after day, the teasing continued. Calvin and Perry swore that Jerry was in love with me, while I remained convinced that it was all a joke.

Evidently, the guys informed Jerry that I hadn't believed what they'd told me, because one day, he stopped me in the hallway. "It's true," he said to me. "I do love you."

In all my high school years, I never had received any declarations of love from a boy. I was horrified and humiliated by the fact that the thing I'd longed for the most had come from the likes of Jerry Slater. Without a word, I turned away from him and bolted down the hallway in the opposite direction.

After that incident, Jerry and I never spoke to each other again. Calvin and Perry stopped teasing me about him. I put Jerry out of my mind.

One night in 2015, I dreamt that I was at a dance. And Jerry Slater came up to dance with me. He had lost his teenage awkwardness, and had become a confident, handsome gentleman with a charming personality. As we danced, I felt him send me a current of energy that both comforted and enlivened me. I knew that my unkindness toward him had been forgiven.

When I awoke, I recalled Jerry's declaration of love, and I was overwhelmed by his sincerity. He had mustered the courage to offer me his heart, and I had rudely rejected his gift. I suddenly understood that he must have felt crushed as he watched me run away from him. No doubt, he went home that afternoon and holed up in his bedroom, nursing the wound to his fragile adolescent psyche.

There had been nothing about what Jerry had said to me that was manipulative or self-serving. He had genuinely cared for me. My pariah status as a smart girl hadn't mattered to him. He had loved me for who I was.

So, I opened my heart to finally receive the love that he had offered so many years earlier, cherishing it for the rare gift that it had been.

Another post-injury dream allowed me to unburden myself of a wrongful act I had committed as a very young child.

One of my elementary school classmates was a nice little boy named Toby Smith. When we students came back from our holiday break in January of our first-grade year, many of the children brought along toys they'd received for Christmas. Toby brought in a funny little clown. When you pulled the clown's string, it did something amusing.

As the rest of us first-graders found this animated clown to be highly entertaining, Toby's Christmas present ended up being passed from one eager child to another. Never in my life had I received such a cute and silly gift, and I couldn't wait to get my hands on the toy. But the first time I pulled the clown's string, it broke. The clown could no longer do his amusing trick.

Frightened and ashamed, I quickly put down the toy and

walked away, so that no one would know I'd been the one to break it. A few minutes later, Toby came to claim his toy. I saw the dismay on his face when he discovered that his Christmas gift had been broken. I felt terrible, but I could not muster the courage to confess to him that I'd been the one to ruin it.

My guilt lasted for several days. Then it dissipated, and I completely forgot about the incident. A few years later, Toby Smith's family moved out of our school district, and I never saw him again.

That tiny failure to own up to an accident must have weighed on my soul for decades. But a dream allowed me address that old wrong.

The images in the dream were unusually vivid and clear, as if I had traveled through time and space into another dimension. Toby and I met as mature adults. We went on a peaceful walk together, talking quietly. I said to Toby, "I want to let you know that I was the one who broke your toy."

He smiled at me. It was okay. I could see that he held nothing against me.

In the early years of my career as a therapist, I had a young client named Carrie. She was the product of her Caucasian mother's extramarital affair with a Polynesian man, and was the only mixed-race child in her family. She had endured terrible abuse in her dysfunctional household. As an adult, she had gone on to suffer atrocities at the hands of husbands and boyfriends.

Carrie trusted no one in her life. She had no reason to. She often tested my trustworthiness through behavior that tried my patience. She found her life so unbearable that, time and again, I had to coax her off the brink of suicidal behavior.

One day several years after I sustained my brain injury, I was doing some in-depth housecleaning. As I sorted through a collection of old cassette tapes, I came across a tape Carrie had given me. In an effort to soothe her chronic state of agitation, she had purchased a tape of tranquil music. She had been so impressed with its calming effects that she had made a copy of the tape for me.

I'd had no contact with Carrie for several decades. But as I played that old cassette tape, I had a strange experience of our spirits reconnecting in an uncanny and powerful way. For a few moments, it was as if she was right there with me.

I recalled a day during a therapy session when Carrie folded her arms on my desk and rested her head on them, looking up at me with her big brown Polynesian eyes. And I saw the gaze of a trusting child looking at her beloved mother. The following session, Carrie confided in me that, for a few moments, she had indeed felt like I was her mother.

As I listened to the tape, I recognized for the first time how much Carrie had honored me when she'd given me her trust. I felt deeply touched. Now, I listen to that tape once or twice a month when I need to calm my own agitation. At those times, I always think of Carrie.

Several years after my injury, I had the painful experience of someone responding unkindly when I expressed frustration about my vision problems. Her insensitive words hit me hard. For a short while, I felt alone in the world, unsupported in my struggle to cope with my brain injury. Then a memory came to me from forty years earlier.

My daughter Chantelle was born with a disfiguring birth defect. A nest of excess blood vessels called a "cavernous hemangioma" had formed in her right nostril and cheek, distorting the contours of her beautiful little face. The first few doctors I consulted told me there was nothing that could be done to correct the problem.

Heartbroken, I imagined my daughter having to go through life with a disfigurement. Chantelle was such a happy baby. I wondered what would happen to her cheerful disposition when she grew old enough to be conscious of her appearance. For months, I lived with constant grief.

While the cavernous hemangioma was primarily a cosmetic concern, it also put Chantelle at risk for losing large amounts of blood. Once when an insensitive doctor tried to diagnose her condition by poking the mass in her nostril with a needle, a river of blood gushed out. As the doctor offered nothing to stem the flow, I grabbed one of Chantelle's diapers from her diaper bag and held it to her face. Back in the car, I cradled my still-bleeding baby in my arms and sobbed.

Sometimes, Chantelle's hemangioma started bleeding during the night. When I'd go to pick her up from her crib in the morning, I'd find my baby lying in a pool of blood, her sheets and blankets soaked.

I soon discovered the variety of ways other people respond to such a heart-wrenching situation. Some offered tepid or insensitive comments. Others, having full awareness of Chantelle's birth defect, said nothing at all. I felt alone in my sorrow.

My husband Larry and I were, at the time, best friends with a couple named Jim and Peggy. Peggy and I had been pregnant with our baby girls at the same time, and our shared experience had bonded us together. Her daughter had been born, in perfect health, three weeks after Chantelle was born. Jim and Peggy were keenly aware of my grief.

One evening when our daughters were just a few months old, Larry and I attended a church function with Jim and Peggy. On the drive home that night, Jim and Peggy sat in the back seat of the car with their baby, while I sat in front with my husband, holding my infant daughter in my arms.

As I'd been raised to conceal vulnerable feelings, I felt ashamed of my weakness when I grieved over Chantelle's condition. I tried to push down my sadness. But that evening, I couldn't hold back the tears as I spilled out my concerns about my baby's birth defect.

For a few moments, there was dead silence in the car. Then, in the darkness, I heard Jim's voice coming from the back seat. "We want you to know, Lois," he said, "that no matter what happens, Peggy and I will be with you through all of this."

I wasn't used to such kindness. I didn't feel worthy of it, and I couldn't fully receive Jim's words at the time. But decades later, when hurting from someone's unkind remarks about my brain injury, I recalled those loving words. This time, I took them in fully, appreciating the depth of the commitment Jim and Peggy had offered. Somehow, those words from the past comforted me in the present, and I felt less alone in the world.

Thankfully, when Chantelle was eight months old, a plastic surgeon removed the hemangioma from her face. A second surgery when she was sixteen fully corrected the problem. Now, almost imperceptible surgical scarring is the only telltale signs of my beautiful daughter's birth defect.

Jim and Peggy ended up moving to another country. Over the years, I lost track of them. Wherever they are now, I thank them for their enduring gift of kindness.

In the heightened awareness of my post-injury years, I sometimes recall events from my past in which someone showered me with praise or compliments in order to get what they wanted from me. I can now see how their sweet words masked their dishonorable intentions. Conversely, I recall other times when a person did or said something that puzzled me, or even angered me. In my new clarity, I can see how their actions were done for the sake of my wellbeing.

Throughout my years as a social work student, I did a number of internships in various community agencies, where I worked alongside agency staff. During the senior year of my undergraduate program at Goshen College, I was sexually harassed by a predatory employee of the agency in which I was completing an internship.

I was an incredibly naïve young woman at the time, and didn't understand what was happening to me. The harassment culminated in a sexual assault that occurred about six weeks before my college graduation.

I was too ashamed and afraid to report what had happened to me, and I tried to go about my normal routine as a mother, wife, and student. But the experience left its terrible aftereffects in my life, creating an ugly emotional scar.

Two of my professors, Dr. Bender and Dr. Miller, served as the pillars of the Goshen College social work program. Both were deeply invested in their roles as guides and protectors of the students for whom they arranged internships. While I did not report the sexual assault to them, I later learned that they had found out about it.

Several months after the assault, I started graduate school, still raw and wounded from the terrible experience.

For my final internship in my graduate program, I was placed in a social service agency in my local community. Unbeknownst to me, the director of that agency, Mr. Jackson, had a reputation for being sexually inappropriate with both his female staff and his clients. He had somehow managed to elude any efforts to hold him accountable for his behavior.

I don't know how Dr. Bender and Dr. Miller found out about my placement in that agency, but they did. One day, I received a phone call from Dr. Bender. "Lois, you can't stay there," she insisted. "I've talked with Dr. Miller about this. Mr. Jackson is a sexual predator. I told Dr. Miller that if Lois works in his agency, she's a sitting duck for his abuse."

My two former professors were so concerned about my safety that they began calling the director of my graduate internship program, telling him it was imperative that I be moved to another agency. I had begun to experience Mr. Jackson's strange behavior, and was confused by what he was doing. But I didn't have an immediate sense of danger. I was, at the time, exhausted by my long months in graduate school, and wasn't eager to go through the disruption of being moved.

The director of the internship program, who knew nothing of Mr. Jackson and his sordid reputation, refused to move me without a valid reason. Undaunted, Dr. Bender and Dr. Miller continued to lobby on my behalf, making pests of themselves.

While Mr. Jackson was busy playing head-games with me, he was, at the same time, refusing to comply with what the university required of him as my supervisor. This eventually presented a valid reason for the university to move my internship to a different agency.

Mr. Jackson feigned innocence, acting as if he was a victim of a great injustice. He blamed me for what happened, and the whole situation became very unpleasant. At the time, I was miffed at my former professors for creating such a hassle for me in my final months of graduate school.

Several years after sustaining my brain injury, memories of that time popped up, and I suddenly saw with great clarity what Dr. Bender and Dr. Miller had done for me. Looking back on the scene as an older, wiser woman, I saw that Mr. Jackson's strange behavior had been the early stages of his grooming me to be his next victim. Had I suffered a second sexual assault in such a short period of time, the effects would have been psychologically debilitating.

I suddenly understood that Dr. Bender and Dr. Miller had foreseen all this, and that was why they had worked so doggedly to spare me further trauma. The realization took my breath away. I felt great tenderness for those two professors, deeply touched by their heroic efforts to protect me. Their care for me finally landed in my very grateful heart.

If a brain injury had not slowed down and altered my life, would I ever have had the good fortune to receive all these beautiful gifts from long ago? Or would they have floated on past me, never finding an open heart in which to land?

OLD PAIN, NEW STRENGTH

Like many other women, I've experienced physical abuse as a child, sexual assault as an adult, and a series of emotionally abusive relationships with men. Prior to my brain injury, I worked on all these issues, trying to emerge from the role of victim to that of survivor.

I once heard it said that healing from trauma is like peeling an onion. You peel away one layer of pain, and you think you've resolved your issue. But later, you realize there's a deeper layer to peel away, and then another and another. It seems as if healing is a lifelong process.

Just about the time I thought I was on top of all my issues, a car appeared out of nowhere and plowed into my side, leaving me lying helpless in the middle of the road. And it felt as if that event was just another link in the chain of violent episodes in my life. It felt like the biggest beating down I had ever experienced. I wondered if I was going to exit this life by having the will to live battered out of me. But I knew I didn't want things to end on such a tragic note.

I found I had to deal, not only with the violence of being struck by a car, but also with deeper layers of the onion pertaining to other episodes of violence and abuse. It was too painful to carry unresolved issues from past trauma while coping with brain injury related challenges.

Furthermore, the brain injury seems to have deprived me of some of my psychological defense mechanisms. When things hurt, they hurt harder than they used to. Pain stares me in the face and won't let me get away from it. It demands to be addressed. Toxic relationship patterns become intolerable, and I have no choice but to work on changing unhealthy dynamics.

My husband suffers from bipolar disorder. In his young adult years, he turned to self-medicating through substance abuse. Alcohol played havoc in our relationship the first few years we were together. He quit drinking before we got married.

For two decades, I turned myself inside out trying to smooth out the bumpy road of our relationship. I learned everything I could about bipolar disorder. I cut my husband slack because I knew it was difficult for him to manage his moods. I tried not to trigger angry outbursts. I stuffed down my own pain and anger to keep from causing him stress. But every now and then, my repressed feelings would bubble up to the surface, and there would be an ugly explosion between the two of us.

I've known for quite some time that I have codependent tendencies. Over and over, I have lost my own self when I've allowed another person's problems to become the center of my world. When I was dating my second husband Wesley, he once hurled his car keys into a weedy field in a fit of rage. Instead of leaving him to deal with the results of his behavior, I dutifully waded into the weeds to help him search for the keys, thereby letting him know that I'd never fail to rescue him from the consequences of any destructive impulse he might act upon.

Wesley was prone to showy displays of temper. As the years of our marriage passed, I scurried around trying to fix whatever was upsetting him. One year on his birthday, I heard him having a tantrum in our bedroom. I rushed into the room to find out what was wrong. He yelled that he didn't want to be one year older. I stood there feeling powerless. There were many things I could do to temporarily appease my malcontented husband, but stopping his birthdays from rolling around wasn't one of them.

While caring for another person might be a loving thing to do, codependency is not a noble path to take. Excessive caretaking and rescuing harms other people. It weakens them and inhibits their growth.

Because of Russ's bipolar disorder, I had never expected him to be entirely responsible for his behavior, or to be a fully functioning adult. I made every attempt to be understanding and longsuffering, to convince myself that I could handle my husband's lack of consideration for my rights and needs.

But try as hard as I could, I couldn't stay nice forever. I'd get to the end of my rope, and I'd be the one to lose my temper. After nasty confrontations between the two of us, I'd consider the idea of leaving my husband. Prior to my brain injury, I repeatedly found myself on the precipice of divorce. Whenever I'd bring up the subject with Russ, telling him we both might be happier if we parted ways, he'd promise to work harder on our relationship. However, nothing would change between us.

After my brain injury, I knew I was in no position to leave Russ and live on my own. I'd already been through two divorces, and was aware of the emotional and financial toll they'd taken on me. Whenever I'd look at the possibility of ending my marriage, I could see nothing but hardship ahead of me.

To Russ's credit, he did shoulder more of the load in our marriage after my accident, and he has always been considerate of my brain injury challenges. But old dynamics continued to rumble beneath the surface of our relationship, preventing any true intimacy from growing between us.

For most of our years together, Russ expressed an insatiable desire to spend time alone. In addition to working long hours, he would leave the house for long stretches of time on the weekends. He'd tell me that being alone helped him manage the agitation caused by his bipolar disorder, and I would tell myself that I should respect his need.

However, after my brain injury limited my opportunities to socialize with others, Russ's lengthy absences from the home left me with no meaningful interaction for days on end. The depth of my loneliness was something I'd never known before.

It wasn't until October 2016 that I faced the fact that Russ's bipolar disorder was not the main issue in our relationship. After a particularly unpleasant confrontation between him and me, I had a sudden epiphany. I saw that he and I were playing out a full-blown version of the classic addict/codependent drama, and that my behavior was hurting him as much as his was hurting me.

When I viewed bipolar disorder as the main problem in our marriage, it kept me in a position of pity and powerlessness. But when I looked at our marriage from the perspective of the addict/codependent model, I could suddenly see my way out of the muddle. I couldn't change my husband's behavior, but I could certainly change my role in the drama.

I saw that my lowered expectations and my rescuing behavior was weakening my husband, getting in the way of his emotional and spiritual growth. I had to stop viewing him as a prisoner of his bipolar disorder. I knew I wasn't a prisoner of my brain injury. I was finding ways to cope with and compensate for my challenges. In the same vein, I knew Russ could be creative in finding ways to manage his disorder. It dawned on me that

Russ had as much capacity to grow and change as I did, and that I needed to stand aside to give him room to find his own way and develop his own strength.

For six days, I distanced myself from Russ, asking nothing from him and refraining from any discussion about our marriage. Previously when I'd pulled away from my husband, it was because I was angry. This time, I did it out of love.

I knew I needed to create a vacuum in our relationship. Instead of trying to fix everything myself, I needed to allow Russ the opportunity to engage in thoughts and actions that would bridge the gap between us.

During those six days of emotional separation from my husband, I found a deep peace within myself. I was lonely, but found that I could bear the loneliness. I was completely deprived of any human touch, but found that I could bear that also.

At times, I was conscious of the impulse to do something to reconnect with Russ, but I refrained from acting on that urge. I knew it would abort the important process that was happening between us. I recognized how, over the years, I had endured a million little rebuffs from my husband when I'd tried to meet my need for emotional intimacy. I resolved to stay strong, to allow him to contemplate his own need for connection rather than imposing upon him the way I thought things should be.

I also saw how much I'd overextended myself when I wanted attention, affection, or approval from him or any other person. Inevitably in such cases, I would be ignored, or the person wouldn't reciprocate my overtures. And then I'd suffer the pain of rejection and the loss of dignity. I realized that I could love my husband and others while staying centered in my own personal space.

Stepping back and letting go of expectations left me feeling lighter and clearer, unburdened.

In my state of deep contemplation, I remembered a dream I'd had years earlier. I was standing on the shores of Lake Michigan, on the beach a quarter of a mile from my home. I was there with a man I'd never seen before, and I had no idea who he was. He had an other-worldly glow about him, as if he'd come from another realm. We were able to communicate through reading each other's thoughts.

I felt a deep connection with the man. "Can you and I be together?" I asked him through my thoughts.

And he responded with this thought message: "If you try to connect with me now, all you will get is my anger. You need to wait until the spirit of God moves within me."

As I thought about the dream, it seemed as if it was addressing my relationship with Russ. I knew I needed to wait and allow the spirit to work in both our lives. I saw that I'd been hanging on too hard to my husband, trying too hard to force a connection between us. I could feel myself letting go of him. I could feel our souls separating to travel our own paths. I had the sense that his path was much different than mine. I could also see that growth was possible for him, in his own way, in his own timing.

In the peace and quiet of my own soul, I came to understand that Russ was afraid of intimacy with me. And I felt okay with that. I knew that my suffering from lack of intimacy in a marriage could be eased by maintaining an intimacy with my own soul.

After six days of space between us, Russ requested a time to talk, and I agreed. His first words were angry. Strangely, that didn't hurt me, because I had emotionally taken myself out of reach of any attack. Eventually, he came around to a more heartfelt expression of what he was feeling. He communicated a great deal of remorse for his behavior in our earlier years of marriage, and a desire to make it up to me now. I could sense his genuineness. He wasn't doing this to get himself off the hook, because I'd put no hook into him.

When he was done speaking, I told Russ about my awareness of the addict/codependent dynamic between the two of us, and of my resolve to stop caretaking and rescuing. I was surprised when he readily agreed with my assessment of our relationship. He told me he'd been in my shoes before, that in a previous marriage, he'd tiptoed around a wife who played the addict role in their relationship.

Russ acknowledged that his addictive thought processes had taken a toll on his relationships with others. I was surprised by his level of insight. I realized that when I allowed him the space to do so, my husband could think deeply and figure things out.

I told him our struggle wasn't over, that we would have a tendency to slip back into old patterns from time to time. But, as it turned out, that week of emotional separation followed by an honest discussion marked a turning point in our relationship.

For two decades, I had weakened my husband by not expecting him to be strong. Now, I see his strength steadily increasing, and I am very grateful for that.

Prior to my injury, I dealt with the emptiness in my marriage by spending time in activities away from home. Now, brain injury challenges have cut off many of my opportunities to relate to others. I believe this may be the time for Russ and me to turn toward each other, to deepen our relationship instead of escaping from it.

Russ and I both recognize the importance of us being each other's best friend. Even though we still spend a great deal of time apart, we have started doing more activities together and having more fun together. Like many men, Russ doesn't share the same desire for emotional intimacy that I have. But I see his concern when he thinks we're becoming distant from each other, and I see him take action to correct the problem.

We still have moments of tension and conflict in our marriage. But I am learning to express my anger and hurt feelings right away, rather than letting them simmer and turn into resentment. In adopting this practice, I've had to give up my need to be "nice."

I am learning to be more forthright and clear in telling my husband what I need from him. I am quicker to set a limit when his behavior steps on my toes. As I continue to allow him to take half of the responsibility for the state of our marriage, I am learning that he has more relationship skills than I ever thought he had.

Getting a measure of my needs met within the relationship makes it easier for me to allow Russ the independence he wants. I find that a small amount of "quality time" goes a long way.

When I first met Russ in 1996, I fell deeply in love with the interesting, talented, brilliant man I knew him to be. Having been twice divorced, I'd never had a satisfying long-term relationship with a man. I saw in Russ the potential for the best relationship of my life. However, when things didn't go well between us, I began to think I never would know what it is like to experience a loving marriage.

But now, the potential I saw more than twenty years ago is becoming an actuality. Sometimes, I think it is nothing short of a miracle that two people with brain problems—Russ's bipolar disorder and my injury—have managed to overcome years of turmoil and create a stable relationship that steadily improves with the passage of time. We will always need to be mindful of each other's challenges. But I am deeply grateful for how far we've come.

I am allergic to poison ivy. Horribly allergic. Several summers ago, I unknowingly came into contact with that malevolent plant. I fought the resulting painful, unbearably itchy rash with several types of over-the-counter ointments. When I saw that I was losing the battle, I went to my doctor, who gave me a prescription for prednisone.

Anyone who's undergone corticosteroid treatment for poison ivy can tell you that the medication turns you into a hyperactive insomniac. The ten-day regimen is rough, and seems unending.

But the miserable affliction of poison ivy gave me a strange gift. The prednisone altered my state of mind, giving me unusual perspectives. Under its influence, I did some important journaling about challenging relationships in my life.

One by one, I worked my way through a list of people with whom I felt at odds, or people with whom I'd had a difficult history. With each subject, I started my journaling at a point of anger and pain. I kept writing and writing, allowing the process to carry me where I needed to go. Inevitably, the journaling would take me to a place where I understood the other person's point of view. I could see why they did and said the things I found so troubling. Understanding them allowed for forgiveness.

For days, I continued this project, speeding along under the influence of my medication. By the time I finished the journaling, I was in such an elated mood that I could almost hear singing in the air around me.

The most important journaling I did was about my mother. My relationship with her seemed to have gotten off to a bad start the day I was born. I had entered her life at a time when she was besieged by stress and impossible demands on every side. She was exhausted and depleted. She had no energy to deal with the needs of the seventh squalling infant who'd arrived on the scene.

My naturopathic doctor once used a technique on me that was meant to clear trapped emotions from the body. At the end of the session, she asked me to repeat the affirmation, "I am glad to be alive." When I uttered those words, I felt guilty, as saying them seemed like a betrayal of my mother. It seemed that in celebrating my life, I was being insensitive to the burden that my birth had placed upon her. I felt I owed her an apology.

Early in my childhood, I developed the belief that I was a curse on my mother's life, that she would have been better off without me. About the time I entered elementary school, she began telling me that I had a bad attitude. In an attempt to rectify this character defect in me, she utilized harsh corporal punishment, the only child-rearing tool she seemed to have at her disposal.

Being slapped, knocked around, and beaten with a belt didn't improve my attitude. It only filled me with despair and self-loathing. I began to think of myself as a despicable human being, as a good person would never be deserving of such treatment.

Thankfully, I was not mistreated at school. None of my teachers viewed me the same way my mother did, and school became a safe zone for me. No doubt, that is one of the reasons I stayed in school for as long as I did. Even after graduate school, I continued to take classes of one kind or another.

While my mother's physical attacks did not continue into my adulthood, the emotional assaults did. Once, I was sitting next to her while she was holding a conversation with a woman she had just met. She told this woman that because I'd had temper tantrums as a toddler, I had ruined our family life.

"Without her, we would've had a good family," she confided. Then she added, "But I've forgiven her for that."

I walked away from that encounter in a state of shock, unable to fathom what I'd just heard. I was a mother of three young children at the time. In raising them, I had dealt with many temper tantrums. But I had always believed such behavior was typical of toddlers, and had never thought my children were ruining my life when they acted out. I'd never felt the need to

178

forgive a three-year-old for throwing a fit. And I never would have dreamed of uttering in front of my children the hurtful words my mother had said in front of me.

Once again, I had experienced my mother's contempt toward me. For the next few days, I struggled with thoughts of ending my life.

Although I tried at different points to work out an understanding with my mother while she was still alive, I never succeeded in doing so. When I finally realized that the differences in our personalities and our worldviews created too great of a gulf to be bridged, I sadly let go of the dream of ever being understood or appreciated by my mother.

My father was a quiet man. While he and I never talked much with each other, I sensed that we were kindred spirits. As he approached the end of his life in 2004, I knew it was time for me to say everything I'd ever wanted to say to him. I wrote a letter expressing my appreciation for the many kind and heroic things he'd done for me. I handed him the letter three weeks before he died.

After reading the letter, my father looked surprised, "I never knew I was that kind of man," he said.

I was so glad that I'd told him. At that moment, writing that letter of gratitude felt like the best thing I'd done in my entire life.

After he died, my father appeared in my dreams, which comforted me. I never felt that he'd left me. In my mind and heart, the relationship between our souls continued.

My mother lived for four and a half years after my father passed. Several weeks prior to her death, she suffered a massive stroke, which robbed her of cognitive and motor functions. She was unable to speak or communicate in any manner.

It troubled me deeply that my mother and I never had managed to set things right with each other. I knew I had to do whatever I could to end my relationship with her on a positive note. Knowing that she no longer had the ability to say anything unkind to me, I stood at her bedside, holding her hand, stroking her face, and saying all the loving things I'd never been able to say before.

179

Afterwards, I thought everything was wrapped up between us. I had overcome all the ugliness and had said goodbye to her on a note of love. In my mind, the relationship was over. We had parted ways. We were done with each other.

But several years after my injury, my mother came to me in a dream. She was smiling, her face lit up with an ethereal glow. "You need me as much as I need you," she said. And then she was gone.

The dream startled and overwhelmed me. I knew that my mother had spoken the truth. We both needed the love and understanding of the other. Without it, there would be a void in each of our souls.

Still, I was resentful that she had intruded into my life. Hadn't I done enough for her when I stood at her bedside and spoke those loving words? For months, I struggled with the implications of the dream.

Then came the poison ivy and the prednisone-powered journaling. Through that process, I peeled away more layers of the onion. I came to understand more of who my mother was. I saw her love of and loyalty to the way she was raised. Her frustration when her children rejected those old ways and opted to live in modern times. Her difficulty in comprehending and accepting the changing world. Her impossible task of raising nine children with few resources and little support. Her sadness, her loneliness, her fear. Her errors in judgment that stemmed from misinformation and lack of guidance. Her not knowing what to do with a daughter who wanted more out of life than being a subservient housewife, a girl who was bent on pursuing the male prerogatives of education and career.

At the end of my writing, I felt more compassion for my mother than I'd ever felt before. I suspect that, on the other side, she is working just as hard on understanding me as I have worked on understanding her.

But just when I thought I'd dealt with all my mother issues, I had to peel away yet another layer of the onion, an excruciating layer I hadn't even known was there.

All my life, I've been interested in genealogy. My research on my family tree started when I was a young child. At times when things were peaceful between my mother and me, I plied her for stories about family life when she was growing up.

My mother was proud of her family history. Her ancestors were Anabaptists (later known as the Mennonites and Amish), a religious group that originated in Europe during the era of the Reformation. The mainstream Christian church had considered the Anabaptists to be heretics, and had persecuted them mercilessly in an attempt to eliminate the threat to the established order.

But the Anabaptists stalwartly defended their faith in the face of opposition. When they refused to recant their beliefs, many of them were executed by such methods as drowning, beheading, and burning at the stake. The harried group scurried around Europe trying to find locations where they could build their religious community and live in peace.

My mother spoke of her ancestors in glowing terms, depicting them as people of extraordinary character. I was sure they were all better than I was, and that I never could hope to live up to such a righteous heritage. I knew my mother thought of the Anabaptists as God's chosen people. She was steadfastly loyal to their faith and traditions.

When I was nine or ten years old, I was introduced to *The Martyrs Mirror,* an enormous book filled with stories of my Anabaptist forebears who'd heroically died for their faith. My mother was convinced that we Mennonites would face another era of persecution and martyrdom during our lifetime. She told me that I might need to die for my faith.

Her prediction filled me with dread. I wondered how badly it would hurt to be burned at the stake, how long I'd have to suffer before death mercifully overtook me. I decided that I'd prefer a quick and easy execution, such as beheading. Thankfully, by the time I reached adulthood, I realized that the persecution of the Anabaptists in sixteenth and seventeenth century Europe was not likely to be replicated in modern times.

My mother's Anabaptist ancestors were primarily of Swiss stock. In the early 1700s, they left Switzerland, where they were facing harassment. Crossing the Jura Mountains, they settled in the Franche-Comte region of eastern France, where they were free to found a Mennonite Church and practice their faith undisturbed. A century later, members of this settlement began migrating to America. Most of my mother's relatives migrated to Allen County, Indiana, where they once again founded a Mennonite church.

One day during a story-telling session about her noble ancestors, my mother revealed some shocking information. She told me that one of her great-uncles, the brother of her maternal grandmother, had spent most of his adult life in prison. She said he had married a woman who had already given birth to a child, and that he suspected the child was not biologically his. He resented the little boy and disciplined him harshly. One day, he went too far with his punishment and beat the child to death. My mother told me she had seen this great-uncle after his release from prison. She said he had a strange look in his eyes.

And that was the end of her story. Later, I wished I had asked her more questions, but I suspected that she'd given me all the information she had.

The story about this decidedly unholy Anabaptist ancestor haunted me all my life. I was alone in my contemplation of the sad tale. I never heard it discussed by aunts, uncles, cousins, or grandparents. As far as I knew, none of my siblings had ever heard the story. I don't even know if my father knew about it. Perhaps my mother ended up recounting that unfortunate chapter of family history to the child who begged for stories the most.

Years later, when I was in college, one of my social work professors gave us students an assignment to construct a family tree. We were to work on identifying belief systems and relationship patterns passed from one generation to the next. As this was before the days of easy access to information on the internet, I had only one source of material available to me: my parents.

My mother responded to my request for information by writing down a number of family stories for me. Among the tales of brave immigrants, church-founders, Sunday-School teachers, thrifty farmers, and resourceful housewives, she included several sentences about her grandmother's brother, reiterating what she'd told me during my childhood.

As I grew older, my obsession with genealogy research intensified. Three years ago, using information that had been given to me in list form, I took on the project of drawing a family tree that extended as far back as the 1500s. Pushing my challenged vision as far as it would go, I chipped away on the project every day.

What emerged on my mother's side of the family startled me. I discovered that the Anabaptist ancestors who had migrated from Switzerland to eastern France, and then later to Allen County, Indiana, had become a closed society that largely shut itself off from marrying outsiders. Clusters of siblings in one family married clusters of siblings in another family. Cousins married cousins. The inbreeding was mindboggling. It became impossible to draw anything that resembled a tree. What emerged was more like a tangle of vines.

In April 2017, my husband signed up for the *Ancestry* website to research his own family tree. I thought about my mother's great-uncle, and asked Russ to help me do a little research on that story.

Given my difficulty with handling strong emotion, it was probably unwise for me to delve into such a story. But I wanted to know the whole truth about something that had bothered me since childhood.

I'd never known the first name of my mother's great-uncle. However, from the family tree I'd drawn, I'd learned that his parents were Jacob and Katherine. Jacob was an immigrant from the Anabaptist settlement in eastern France, and Katherine's parents had migrated from that same community a generation earlier.

Through our internet research, Russ and I discovered that Jacob and Katherine's marriage had produced nine children. Katherine died the year following the birth of her youngest child. Shortly thereafter, Jacob married a young woman who'd recently immigrated from his home community in eastern France. They had four more children together.

My husband scoured the census records of Jacob's many sons borne by his two wives, to discover which one had spent time in prison. It seemed as if his research wasn't going to uncover anything, and I began to wonder whether there was any truth in my mother's tragic tale. But then Russ came to the youngest child of Jacob and Katherine, the child whose mother had died when he was a baby. He had a noble Biblical name: Amos.

The 1910 U.S. census listed Amos as a 34-year-old farmer living in Allen County, Indiana, with his 27-year-old wife Sarah. They had been married for a year. They had no children in the household.

Then we discovered that both the 1920 and 1930 census records listed Amos as an inmate in the Indiana State Prison. The information made my heart pound. We had identified the great-uncle from my mother's long-ago story.

But we could find no record of the child that Sarah had supposedly brought into their marriage, the child that Amos had supposedly beaten to death. Had Sarah been pregnant at the time of the 1910 census? Had the unfortunate child been born and then killed sometime between 1910 and 1920? But other records indicated that neither Amos nor Sarah had ever produced offspring.

Puzzled by our lack of findings, we turned to old newspaper records. Immediately, a flurry of newspaper articles from 1910 popped up, pertaining to Amos. The articles were published, not just in Allen County where he lived, but in other Indiana counties and in different states across the country. As we began reading the articles, we discovered that my mother's brief account of the death of a child had been entirely wrong. The child in question had not belonged to Amos's wife.

The story that unfolded in the newspapers was so horrifying that Russ and I couldn't stomach it all at once. We had to read the articles in installments. They described a murder so heinous, so grotesque, so depraved that, according to the coroner who examined the victim's body, it was one of the most brutal murders in the annals of crime.

The story stretched the bounds of human imagination. Said my husband, "It's a Gothic horror story. It's like a Charles Dickens tale as told by Edgar Allen Poe."

According to the articles, my mother's great-uncle Amos was a well-to-do farmer who expertly managed his sizable acreage. His fences and outbuildings were in pristine condition. He and Sarah lived in an impeccably clean and tidy house. His neighbors reported that although he wasn't friendly, Amos was honest in all his business dealings.

But they described him as money-mad. As a way of obtaining cheap farm labor, Amos and Sarah had taken an orphan into their home in February 1910, from an institution in neighboring Ohio. The twelve-year-old boy's name was Claude.

Claude was old enough and strong enough to do the chores around the farm. However, according to the neighbors and the boy's schoolteacher, Claude was a slow learner, unable to comprehend what was expected of him. Apparently, the boy's failure to complete his assigned chores enraged Amos time and again.

Neighbors began to suspect that Amos was mistreating the boy, as they could hear the child's anguished screams. Eventually, the sheriff was called out to investigate. An advocate from the Humane Society became involved in the case. He deemed that Amos and Sarah's home was not a suitable place for young Claude to live. He removed him from the home and returned him to the orphanage.

Amos then went to court, petitioning the judge to place Claude back into his care. Family and church members, including his pastor, accompanied Amos and testified to his good character. Even though the Humane Society advocate protested adamantly, the judge ruled in Amos's favor. Young Claude was returned to Amos's care, despite the fact that he cried piteously and begged not to go back.

Amos assured the judge that he would treat the child well. But in no time at all, the old patterns resumed. Claude repeatedly failed to perform his duties to Amos's satisfaction, and Amos continued his cruel punishments.

On an evening in July, five months after Claude's initial placement in the household, Amos came home from a trip to town to discover that the boy hadn't finished his assigned chores. Enraged, he brutally assaulted him. Despite the fact that his wife begged him to stop, he continued to punish Claude until the child breathed his last breath.

Amos and Sarah attempted to revive Claude, but when they failed to do so, they concocted an alternate story about the boy's death. They took off his clothing and rubbed it in the filth from the cow stall. Then they re-dressed the body and summoned the doctor, explaining to him that Claude had been kicked to death by a cow.

The doctor called the coroner, who, upon examining the body, recognized that the child had been murdered. The final cause of death was listed as head trauma. But the coroner said that if Claude hadn't died that night, he would have died within a few days, from sepsis in wounds that had been previously inflicted. He stated that Amos had been "killing the child by inches." He described the body as "horribly mutilated."

One newspaper article catalogued the nature and number of the wounds Amos had inflicted on the child's body. I will not repeat the grotesque details in this book. It appeared that the honest, industrious, well-to-do man who managed his farm so capably had gone completely berserk. He'd gone farther out of his mind than anyone could imagine a human being going.

I can't express the horror I felt after reading the newspaper articles. I spent days in a state of shock and turmoil. I couldn't concentrate on my housework. I couldn't write more than a paragraph or two at a time. I could hardly eat. At night, I lay awake while the details of the gruesome story played over and over in my mind.

I felt deeply ashamed of the fact that I was related to a man like Amos. Having a notorious murderer in my family tree sickened and revolted me. I couldn't stand to look in the mirror, knowing that Amos's family had provided some of the DNA that formed my appearance. I felt dirty and contaminated. I wanted to jump into a vat of disinfectant to cleanse myself.

Old feelings of self-loathing took hold of me. I desperately tried to remember who else I was, other than a product of my ancestry. I tried to remind myself of what good things I'd accomplished in my life.

Repeatedly, I asked myself how the murder could have happened. How was there this one piece of rotten fruit among the supposed paragons of virtue in my family tree? How had these church-founding, chosen-by-God Anabaptist families produced a heinous criminal?

The newspapers stories suggested that, to a degree, the family had been complicit in the murder. Amos's "people" had accompanied him to court, vouching for his character. Hadn't they known him for who he was? Why had they lobbied to place a vulnerable child in the care of a dangerous man?

How, I wondered, had this widely publicized story been reduced to only a few sentences in my mother's family lore? And how had the story become so distorted in her mind? Perhaps Amos's family never knew the full details of his crime. Perhaps they hadn't want to know. Perhaps they never had the opportunity to read the newspaper articles that my husband and I discovered more than a hundred years later.

Some of the specifics of Amos and Sarah's home life, as recounted in the newspaper stories, were eerily similar to conditions in my childhood, the lifestyle, folkways, and attitudes passed down to my mother by her parents and grandparents. Reading those details made my skin crawl.

However, something more significant in the articles caught my attention. When arrested, Amos initially had not understood that he was in deep trouble for the murder of the orphan child. He had explained to the authorities that his brutal treatment of the boy was his way of disciplining him. He had seemed surprised that anyone would view that behavior as heinous.

My mother had also believed that harsh corporal punishment was a normal and proper response to a child's misbehavior. I remembered the matter-of-fact stories about my grandmother beating my mother's older sister. And I remembered my mother beating me.

I recalled the image of her coming at me brandishing a belt, her eyes ablaze with anger. At those times, I had thought she wanted to kill me, to obliterate my disgusting presence from her life. I had imagined she would have done it if she could have gotten away with it. I know now that my mother didn't have murderous intentions, but that is how my child mind interpreted the rage in her eyes.

The story of the murder and the memories of my mother's harsh corporal punishment melded together in my mind. I remembered how anxious the repeated beatings had made me, how afraid I'd been that my mother's ever-vigilant eyes would catch me in wrongdoing that would justify further punishment. I could only imagine how terrified young Claude had been of Amos.

It felt as if my family's violent history had me in a headlock. My husband wanted me to feel better quickly, to put the terrible story out of my mind. But I knew I had to pass through a very dark tunnel of pain before I could come to a point of peace and clarity. "Just give me time," I kept telling him.

For three days in a row, I walked down to Lake Michigan to sit by the water, hoping the tranquil surroundings would soothe my troubled mind. The following Sunday, I went to the chapel room in my church, where I lit candles, prayed, and cried. My father's quiet presence in my life had often counterbalanced my tumultuous relationship with my mother. Over and over, I called upon his spirit to help me through the crisis.

Then, something changed. Something nudged me out of my agitation into a more dispassionate frame of mind. An odd but compelling thought whispered to me, "Look at this story from the vantage point of a cultural anthropologist."

One thing I'd learned in my college cultural anthropology class was this: when we view an unfamiliar culture from the outside, we often see practices that appear crazy at best and horrifying at worst. But to the people living within the culture, the practices in question are considered to be normal, essential to their way of life.

Every culture has its strengths and weaknesses. We stand in awe of the Aztecs and Incas, whose achievements seem so far ahead of their time. Yet, we recoil at their practice of human sacrifice.

When I donned my makeshift anthropologist hat, I could see many strengths in my mother's family culture: courage, industriousness, thriftiness, resourcefulness, service to the community. But I could also see a culture of violence against children, a "spare the rod and spoil the child" philosophy taken to extremes. I could see the belief that harsh corporal punishment of children produces upright and moral adults, and that such punishment needs to be escalated if compliance isn't readily achieved. I could see the fear of nonconformity, and the belief that any semblance of evil needs to be stamped out immediately.

I recognized the mindset that had set the stage for the murder of the orphan boy. And I could see how the same belief system had produced my mother's harsh treatment of me.

I could understand why, in the custody hearing for young Claude, Amos's family had testified to his good character. No doubt, they had viewed him as an honest, upright man who dutifully administered discipline to a disobedient child. They might have seen him as a negligent parent if he had failed to punish young Claude for his shortcomings.

I suspected that Amos was not an anomaly in his family. Most likely, he was treated harshly as a child. How else would he have learned such brutal forms of punishment? I suspected that, when punishing Claude for failure to do his chores, he had taken accepted family practices to bizarre and lethal extremes.

The fact that Amos's wife Sarah had witnessed months of brutality without seeking help from outsiders astonished me. Perhaps she'd been terrified of her husband. But I suspected there had been another factor in play. Women in the Amish and Mennonite community during that era were taught to be docile and subservient to men.

Sadly, that era extended to the years of my childhood. My mother accused me of having too strong a will, and she vowed to break it. She said she was afraid I would use my strong will against my husband someday. She wanted to render me incapable of standing up in any way against a husband's authority. Such a belief system was probably so deeply engrained in Sarah that she stood by helplessly while her husband carried out his despicable acts.

In contemplating all this, I understood that loyalty to a culture can blind a person to its weaknesses. I recognized that my mother's harshest acts represented her unthinking devotion to the family norms she held so dear.

In a newspaper article written several days after the murder, the reporter painted a picture of the sun rising over Amos's pristine farm, an idyllic pastoral scene. He then described the scene of the child's fresh grave, the only evidence that something horrifying had happened at the peaceful homestead. His journalistic piece served as a powerful metaphor for the contrast of light and darkness in my family's culture.

I am not suggesting that the culture of violence against children was unique to my mother's family. I recall a day in my third-grade public school classroom when my enraged teacher chased a boy around the room with a wooden paddle. Two dozen eight-year-olds watched this scene in terror, each wondering, *What will happen to me if I step out of line?*

Then, in fifth grade, the entire class witnessed our teacher grabbing a hardbacked notebook from a student and beating him with it. Under current laws, both teachers would have been fired, if not arrested.

Struggling with the murder story opened something that had been clenched like a fist inside me. It brought up depths of pain that I hadn't known were possible. But it was helpful to see the culture of violence for what it was, the culture where strict adherence to rules and harsh punishment for disobeying those rules took precedence over loving relationships.

The story prompted me to do a great deal of forgiving. I had to. I knew that forgiveness was the only thing that would carry me out of the dark tunnel of suffering into the light. In my distress, I called aloud to both Amos and my mother, "I forgive you." Afterwards, my only feeling for my ancestors was compassion, overwhelming compassion for the people who lived under the influence of such a misguided ideology.

I also had to forgive myself for my own shortcomings. When my children were babies, I resolved to raise them differently than I'd been raised. I knew I didn't want to inflict on them the physical and psychological pain that I had experienced as a child. I have a photo of myself sitting with an infant on my lap and a two-year-old on the arm of my chair, his head resting against my shoulder. Both children are sleeping soundly while I am reading a book on child development.

I know I fell far short of perfection as a mother. I never was able to live up to the standards I set for myself. But at least I was able to identify childrearing standards different from those of my ancestors. I was fortunate to be influenced by information to which they didn't have access.

After recovering from the acute agony surrounding the discovery of the murder story, I recalled something my mother had told me years earlier. She had described a scene from when I was a toddler, a moment when she said to herself, "That is a sunshiny child." Fleetingly, she had recognized a shining spirit within me, the spirit that each of us have by birthright.

Throughout the following years of harshness and trauma, my sunny spirit was driven deep inside me, hunkering down for cover. I'm not sure my mother ever saw it again. Perhaps she and I will someday meet on the other side, shining spirit to shining spirit.

I felt deeply for the orphan boy who had suffered so much in his short life, a life that was snuffed out before he had the opportunity to grow into the adult he was meant to be. I wanted to do something to commemorate him. My husband helped me set up a garden angel in a vine-covered nook in our yard, a shrine to young Claude and all the other child victims of the culture of violence.

I've come to terms with my family's history of violence. I've lived through my part of the sad story. I've done my best to keep from passing that legacy on to my children. The trauma is over now. I can move on. May any remaining scars render me more compassionate toward the suffering of others.

FINDING THE PATH

While dusting the shelves on my computer desk one summer afternoon in 2017, I picked up an object that had been sitting there for more than a decade. It was a small picture frame holding a quote.

I had dusted that frame countless times before, picking it up and setting it back into place without giving it much thought. But that day, the quote caught my attention. I stared at it sadly, a rush of memories coming back to me.

In the late 1990s and early 2000s, I had received frequent energy healing sessions from a gifted practitioner named Wanda. After one session, she conveyed to me the words that had come to her while working on me: *Now is the time to swim in the waters of my soul's purpose.*

Those words had thrilled me. I was sure they portended something monumental that was about to happen in my life. So, I typed Wanda's quote in an elegant font, framed it, and set it on my desk.

And I waited and waited for the magical moment when my lofty life purpose would be revealed to me. I was certain the day would come when my rugged path would lead me to tranquil waters, where I would swim blissfully for the rest of my life, fulfilling my soul's purpose, unimpeded by any further obstacles.

Of course, nothing of that sort ever happened.

For many years, I had considered the concept of *path* to be synonymous with *vocation.* Essentially, I had defined my life's journey by the type of work I was doing.

My first sense of vocational path came when I was around ten years old. One Sunday evening, a man from a Mennonite church in northern Indiana came to speak at our little church in Beanblossom. He presented a slide show on a new facility that had been built in his community, Oaklawn Mental Health Center.

As he talked about the center's work with the mentally ill, his words and pictures moved my young heart. I was a sad, scared child who knew what it was like to suffer emotional pain. I felt compassion for Oaklawn Center's troubled patients. I wanted to help them.

However, my interest in becoming a mental health professional went underground for a while. In high school, I discovered my talent for writing, and my senior English teacher encouraged me to follow that vocational path. When I confided in her my interest in a mental health career, she told me I was too sensitive to deal with other people's problems.

At the time I entered college, I had no idea what I wanted to do with my life. After completing one year, I dropped out to get married, then returned part-time after my three children were born. Faced with the need to choose a major, I ended up considering two options: English and Social Work. And I chose the latter, picking up my childhood intention of pursuing a career in mental health.

I've always believed that was a good decision for me, although it took me a while to settle into that career. I spent time employed in other areas of social work, such as foster care, adoption, and working with victims of domestic violence. But mental health always seemed to be the best fit for me.

About eight years into my career, I considered the idea of jumping off that track to pursue a completely different line of work. While still employed as a clinical social worker, I completed schooling to become a Certified Massage Therapist. After that, I pursued training in energy healing, and became a Certified Healing Touch Practitioner.

However, these new vocations never replaced my primary career. They became secondary employment for me. For ten years, I operated a part-time massage and energy healing practice out of my home in Goshen.

As I left young adulthood and entered middle-age, I became more conscious of myself as a spiritual being on a journey, with specific work to do during my time on the planet. I became rather self-important about this.

In the late 1990s, I began to think that taking on an administrative position in a social service agency was the next step on my spiritual path. Just as soon as that intention entered my mind, a series of serendipitous happenings led me right to the type of job I was seeking. It all seemed to happen magically. As

I faced my new endeavor, I felt a great sense of destiny.

Of course, I had to give my employer notice before leaving my position as a therapist, and it took a month to make the transition between the two jobs. As I finished my final weeks in my old position, my wonderful new job was always on my mind. I felt certain that I was on the brink of something monumental.

One day, the mother of one of my teenage clients came in to talk to me. She brought with her another one of her children, a two-month-old baby girl.

When the mother entered my office, the baby was sleeping in her carrier. But a few minutes into the session, she woke up. Her mother lifted her out of the carrier and held her.

That baby girl looked for all the world like a little Buddha, with a round bald head and big chubby cheeks. Her sleepy eyes stared in confusion at the strange surroundings in my office. Then her gaze fell on me, and she burst into laughter.

It wasn't just a smile or a gurgle or a chuckle. It was peals of deep-down belly laughter that went on and on. Her bewildered mother tried to quiet her. "She's never done this before," she told me.

As it turned out, the mother and I were unable to carry on a conversation, because every time I opened my mouth to speak, the baby's peals of loud laughter reverberated throughout my office.

I had the distinct impression that the little Buddha baby's spirit sensed something ridiculous in me. There I sat, feeling so self-important about the new job I was about to start. And every time I spoke, her laughter said to me, "You are so full of bull!"

I soon discovered why that administrative job was so easily obtained. It wasn't because I'd been providentially led to the position. It was because the culture in that agency was so toxic that they were unable to retain administrative staff. Two years and eight months later, I resigned from that position under very stressful circumstances and returned to my work as a therapist.

During my training for massage therapy and energy healing, I was introduced to the concept that trauma and repressed emotions lodge themselves, not only in the brain, but in the tissues of the body. This new information lit up my mind with all kinds of ideas, and I became dogged in my quest for more knowledge on the subject.

Pursuing this aspect of healing work became my focus for the next thirteen years. I pictured myself creating a practice that combined my psychotherapy knowledge with my massage and energy healing skills, allowing me to work with both body and mind to relieve my clients' emotional troubles. I imagined that this approach could cure all of life's ills.

I practiced a little of this type of work with my clientele in my home business, although most of them weren't interested in unburdening their minds. They simply wanted a relaxing massage. I tried pitching my combination of skills to my supervisors at the counseling center in which I was working, but administration was concerned about liability issues that might come with this unusual form of therapy.

However, I did not give up hope. I believed that, at any moment, my rocky path would open into the blissful waters I'd so long envisioned. And there would lie the perfect opportunity to do the one big thing that would validate my existence on this planet. Sometimes, I even imagined that my path would take me to distant lands and exotic locations.

This whole quest turned into quite an ego trip for me. When I experienced unusual phenomena during my energy healing training, I believed I was developing special gifts. I imagined I was on the way to becoming a great healer. I enjoyed the thrill of believing in my magical destiny. It made me feel vibrant and alive.

I pictured myself continuing my healing practice well into my senior years. I envisioned myself becoming an elderly person admired by others, contributing to society long after the age when most people retire.

I started viewing my ordinary practice in the field of mental health as something I had outgrown. In my mind, it was time for a new chapter, a time to become the healer I was truly meant to be. With a great deal of intensity, I meditated and prayed about finding the perfect career opportunity that would combine my psychotherapy and energy healing skills.

Through a series of serendipitous events in 2005-2006, I landed a position in a hospice program in southwest Michigan.

While interviewing for the job, I proposed my idea of incorporating energy healing into my work with patients and their families. The agency's administrators were not only willing to have me bring such skills to the position, they were excited about the prospect.

Elated, I believed my dream job had finally landed in my lap. Everything seemed to fall into place very quickly. In a week's time, I resigned from my old position, accepted my new position, sold my old house in Goshen, and bought a new one in Saint Joseph.

In making the physical move from Goshen to Saint Joseph, I believed I was making great strides on my life's journey. I was convinced that God was illuminating the path from Indiana to Michigan, and that things would continue to fall into place for me.

But they didn't. At the end of my first day on the new job, the agency staff was informed of a shakeup at the top levels of administration. The long-term CEO had been dismissed.

In short order, this shakeup began to affect every layer of the agency's administration. Supervisors were fired, while others resigned. Frontline workers had no idea what to expect from day to day. Just as I was trying to learn a new job in a new community, the workplace became so chaotic that I had no one to teach me what I needed to know. My exhilaration turned into despair.

Furthermore, while some people in the organization welcomed the idea of me incorporating my energy healing skills into my work, others were adamantly opposed to it. My desire to do the work I loved became a source of controversy within the agency.

As conditions worsened for me in the workplace, I became increasingly despondent, sorely regretting my decision to exchange my stable life in Indiana for the mess I'd walked into. I floundered in the hospice program for five months, until I was offered a therapist's position in a community mental health center in a neighboring city.

After having glided along the seemingly illuminated path to the hospice position, I stumbled into my second Michigan job feeling battered and bruised. But I was back in the field of mental health, where it seemed I'd always belonged, and I wondered at the decision I'd made to leave it. As a mature clinician, I did the best work of my career during the four years I worked at that agency.

It took me two years to recover from my hasty, ill-advised move from Indiana to Michigan. I often walked the few blocks from my house to Lake Michigan, where I'd stare at the water and ask a plaintive question: "Why am I here?"

The multitude of problems associated with my move to Michigan put a damper on my magical thinking. But I never completely gave up the hope that some wonderful destiny was awaiting me a few steps ahead on my path.

Then came the day when a car slammed into me, knocking me down in the middle of the road. And it felt as if my path ended right there. While an ambulance came to pick up my injured body and carry it to the emergency room, there was no roadside assistance available to pick up my broken spirit and set it back on course. My journey was over. I was done.

As I struggled with the challenges of my brain injury, it seemed pointless to stick around in this life when I could no longer accomplish anything important. Time and again, I asked God the same question I'd asked the lake: "Why am I here?"

Sometimes, this question involved a great deal of anger. I'd demand to be given an answer about the purpose of my continued existence on the planet. While I had no intention of taking my own life, I often hoped that I wouldn't have much longer to live. I couldn't fathom hanging on another twenty or thirty years in my condition.

I can hardly put into words how difficult it was to let go of the goals and purposes I was pursuing at the time of my accident. The change in my identity, from a would-be healer to a fragile patient, happened instantaneously, so quickly that I couldn't fathom what had occurred. It took me a long while to accept the fact that my old self was gone. I kept thinking that, someday, I would wake up from my brain-injury daze and pick up my journey where I'd left off.

Many nights, I lay awake, the emotional pain feeling like a massive tumor inside my chest and abdomen. I'd try to breathe into the tumor of pain, attempting to understand it, to find my way through it. And when I'd reach the heart of the pain, it would feel unbearable. Letting go of my old dreams felt like death, an awful, agonizing death.

One day while cleaning my bedroom closet, I found a storage container of forms I'd used in my massage therapy and energy healing practice in Goshen. Nostalgia washed over me as I thought about a time in my life when I was filled with hope and enthusiasm. Sadly, I threw away most of the material I knew I'd never use again. But I saved a few forms, telling myself that a day might come when I would resume my healing practice.

Then my brain power began to grow dim from the effort of sorting the container's contents, and the eye strain made me feel sick. Reality hit me. In all likelihood, the only purpose I'd ever find for those old forms was using the back side for scrap paper.

Another day, I came across an ornate bookmark someone had given me many years earlier. The following words were written on it: *You are a woman of wisdom, courage, strength, compassion, and creativity. Go forth with the fire of confidence in your heart, kindle it with care, and never let its brilliant flame go out!*

Those words tore at my heart. They described the powerful woman I'd aspired to be at the time I had received the gift. But I no longer identified with that sentiment. Furthermore, I had no use for a bookmark, as I was no longer a reader of books.

For years after my injury, I experienced periods of sorrow and longing, even though I wasn't always sure what I was longing for. "What is it that I miss so much about my old life?" I kept asking myself. "What is it that I yearn to recapture?"

One autumn day in 2015, I took a walk to the lake. I lay on a bench swing near the water, gazing up at the blue sky and the sparkle of sunlight on the golden leaves of a nearby tree. I allowed myself to lapse into longing, recalling memories from the years prior to my injury.

Suddenly, I realized it wasn't so much what I'd been doing during that era, it was how I'd been feeling. The key word that came to my mind was *potential*. I had believed myself to be someone with the *potential* to do important work on the planet.

Even if nothing special or brilliant was happening in the present moment, I had always believed in the possibility of such things happening in the future.

Then the accident had occurred, robbing me of any sense of potential in my earthly life. With the brain injury, I couldn't imagine doing anything more than surviving until my soul left my body and moved on to the potential offered in the afterlife. I no longer felt like a vibrant woman whose life in this world held possibilities. Hope for the future had curled up inside me and died.

While I know that wishful thinking never can carry me back to where I was, a part of me still longs to ignite a lingering spark of my old belief, so that I can once again feel the excitement of viewing myself as a person with potential. But I've had to admit to myself that my old ways of thinking about potential involved a great deal of fantasy.

When I was in high school and college, frantically trying to prove my worth by chasing academic success, my teachers would occasionally say such things as, "You can do anything you want to in life."

I have finally admitted to myself that my teachers were wrong, that I never did have the potential to do everything I wanted to do. No human being does. I never possessed the intellect to go far in the fields of math or science, even though I would have liked to. While I've enjoyed painting and sculpting as hobbies, I was never talented enough to become a professional artist. I would have loved a career in music or acting, but nature has not endowed me with such gifts.

Even in my chosen profession, I was not capable of doing everything I set out to do. I was too sensitive to endure the politics and the competitive environment I faced when in an administrative position. I was never outgoing enough to do well in networking and marketing.

I've had to question the popular ideas of "thinking big" and "following your dreams." In my case, such thinking led to unrealistic expectations. I can recall many times when I soared into flights of fancy while pursuing lofty goals, only to experience emotional crashes when things didn't work out the way I imagined they would.

I know full well that it is time for me to stop thinking about potential in terms of doing something grand. Instead of reaching for the stars, it is time for me to find satisfaction in doing down-to-earth tasks. I now aspire to be one of the billions of people on this planet who live noble lives as they carry out their ordinary work with courage and devotion.

In times of clarity, I can see that each moment of my life holds potential. Some time ago, I heard the phrase, "Let life happen through you." I don't know who coined that saying, so I am unable to give that person the proper credit. But I appreciate his or her words. The idea deeply resonates with me, as I believe it is now the way I am meant to live: to allow life to happen rather than trying to force it into the shape of my desires and fantasies.

I notice now that whenever I strain and struggle to make things happen, my life feels frantic. At such times, I begin falling apart, both emotionally and cognitively.

When I look in the rearview mirror of my life, I can see countless times in which I've tried to force things to happen. I can see myself swimming against the current, exhausting my energy, grasping for things out of my reach, trying to make things come to fruition before the time was right. I can see myself snatching experiences that weren't meant to be mine, only to end up in sorrow and disappointment.

I remember all too well how I schemed and connived to capture the attention of my second husband Wesley. My strategy worked, but our relationship didn't. On the day Wesley left me, he said, "Someday, you'll make some man a good wife. But I am not the one."

In entering that ill-advised marriage, I had reached for something that wasn't meant to be mine. And in doing so, I brought pain and disruption, not only to my life, but to the lives of my children as well.

In moments of quiet contemplation, some gentle thoughts about potential have come to me: *Worrying about what I am supposed to be doing with my life only hinders me from moving forward. Practicing mindfulness and embracing each moment will carry me to where I need to go. I am happiest when I am moving with the flow, allowing events to unfold in their own timing.*

Early one morning in the summer of 2017, while lying in bed fretting about my lack of opportunities in the world, a strange piece of advice fluttered into my mind: *Stay in your lane. The opportunities will come.*

I knew exactly what those words meant. In the past, I'd careened all over the road and veered off onto side streets, trying to chase down opportunities that I thought would enhance my life. Such desperate behavior caused me stress back then. It causes even more distress in my post-injury life.

Even with all this new awareness, I've been unable to stop missing my old self and the hopes and dreams I once cherished. For a while, I scolded myself every time I lapsed into longing, telling myself that I should let go of the past and move on. It finally dawned on me that fighting the sadness didn't help. I needed to give myself permission to feel whatever I was feeling, to miss who I used to be.

One day during my brief stint of working in hospice care, I went to a local nursing home to visit an elderly patient who was approaching death. The walls of her room were decorated with stunning portraits of her as a professional dancer in the 1930s. It was hard to believe that the gorgeous young woman posing in her exotic dance costumes was the person now lying in the bed, unable to communicate or do anything for herself.

I imagined that, for years, this woman had sorely missed the beautiful, talented young woman she'd once been. And I will always miss who I was before my brain injury, even though I believe I've grown into a wiser and more mature person since then. I've decided that I can embrace the constantly evolving versions of myself and still miss who I used to be. Whenever the old longing comes up now, I open my heart and breathe deeply, allowing myself to feel the bittersweet sadness about what once was, but is no more.

Although my path in the mental health field has come to an end, it seems that I have reconnected with my high school dream of becoming a writer.

The idea for my first novel, *Daughters of Seferina,* came to me in 1993. Flooded with inspiration, I worked feverishly on the project for a few months, completing about one third of the first draft of the story. But other pursuits quickly took precedence. I started massage therapy training, and couldn't find time for writing while both working and going to school. Then, I had to face my second divorce, which put me in a tailspin for a few years. I shoved my incomplete novel into a drawer, doubting that I ever would finish it.

My urge to write lay dormant for a decade, until my first children's book alighted in my mind in 2003. After that, the ideas kept coming. Despite working fulltime in clinical social work, maintaining a part-time massage therapy practice, and pursuing my training in energy healing, I occasionally found brief windows of time for writing.

In 2006, I completed the last of my requirements to become a Healing Touch Practitioner. However, I had no time to bask in that achievement before I was presented with the option of completing the additional work required to become a Certified Healing Touch Practitioner.

Strangely, I balked against taking those final steps. My resistance baffled me. Why was I being so stubborn about this? Was it simply because I was worn out from all the hard work, tired of jumping through hoops? That didn't seem like me. I'd always been willing to face hard work, and had been a proficient hoop jumper.

For several days, I contemplated my reluctance to commit to the additional work, until the true source of my resistance came to me. While finishing the last round of my Healing Touch studies, I had been deeply involved with scribbling down another novel that had been rolling through my mind, *My Truest Companion.* I was afraid that if I committed myself to additional work with the Healing Touch program, *My Truest Companion* would suffer the same fate as *Daughters of Seferina.* It would be set aside, and would never come to completion.

When I fully understood the cause of my resistance, I realized that, even though I loved energy healing, I loved writing just a tiny bit more. I was no longer willing to allow writing to take a back seat in my life.

So, I made a deal with myself. I would put my Healing Touch requirements on hold until I finished the first draft of *My Truest Companion.* Then I would put everything I had into completing the work for my certification. And that is what I did.

When I moved to Michigan, intent on expanding my work as an energy healer, the opportunities I'd hoped for disappeared. Instead, I gravitated toward writing, finding myself in the company of other writers. And after my injury, when all other vocational options were taken from me, I was left with only the writing.

Am I still on a path? I've sometimes wondered. *Can I be on a path if I'm sitting here at home, spending hours in solitude, doing little more than housework, gardening, and a bit of writing? Does this count?*

However, I don't find such questions to be as meaningful as I once did. I am coming to understand that our life journeys have less to do with events in the outer life, and more to do with what goes on in the inner world. It is about the growth of the soul.

Thus, I could be bedbound, never leaving my room, and still be on a journey.

Sometimes when I notice a change in my attitude or thought patterns, or when I've conquered some fear, it seems as if I've mastered some difficult terrain, moving a few steps ahead in my soul's journey.

When I was studying at the ashram in Kalamazoo, the spiritual director cautioned us students that, in terms of the outer events of life, the journey would be bumpy from birth to death. I hadn't wanted to belief such a thing when I first heard him say it. I preferred to hang on to my fantasy that my path would eventually lead to sweetness and bliss.

I now know that I never will come to such an idyllic place in the material world. But I know that on the soul's journey, I am capable of moving ahead even when I flounder in the outer events of life.

For seven years after my injury, I experienced powerful surges of envy every time I encountered someone who had become highly trained in the type of healing work I had hoped to pursue. I would feel cheated because my own path to ongoing training had been blocked. One day in 2017, I encountered one such highly trained healer, whom I instantly envied. Then, in the next few moments, he cured me of that envy.

As I listened to him namedrop and refer to techniques he'd learned, I realized that, in doing so, he was creating a barrier between himself and others. When he referred to a fancy-sounding principal that he'd learned from a spiritual teacher, I was astonished. He was describing something I'd learned on my own, a practice that had come from my solitary contemplation, not from an outside source.

In a split second, it came to me that all of us have a very reliable inner teacher available to us. And that the best thing we can do to heal the suffering of others is not to practice techniques, but to offer compassion. I knew that any technique practiced on me had easily been forgotten, while acts of compassion had made lasting impressions. I realized that while my path to further training had been blocked, opportunities to offer compassion would never be taken from me.

Perhaps I did not miss anything at all when my brain injury stopped me from pursuing further education. Perhaps reading books and traveling long distances to sit under the tutelage of a renowned teacher is no longer necessary for my growth. My unique life experiences, including the brain injury, have taught me volumes. And my inner guide is ever reliable to show me the way.

In my mind, I thanked the highly trained, name-dropping, technique-referencing fellow for what he'd taught me. I suspected that if I would have continued my training, I would have ended up sounding exactly like him. It was almost a "there but for the grace of God go I" moment.

One beautiful late-summer afternoon in 2017, I decided to go outdoors for a stroll. On a whim, I abandoned my typical walking path around my neighborhood and crossed the highway to walk in a different part of town. Taking in sights less familiar to me stimulated my spirit, making me feel more alive. And I began contemplating the words I'd heard a few weeks earlier: *Let life happen through you.*

Suddenly, I realized it was time to move beyond merely thinking about those words. It was time to commit to a new way of life. So, as I walked, I spoke my commitment aloud: "I am ready to adopt a new lifestyle. Rather than trying to control life, I will let life happen through me. I will allow life to lead me. I will stop my anxious efforts to prove my worth, to justify my existence on this planet. I will let go of fantasies. They do not come true. They always bring disappointment. What actually happens is always a surprise, and I will accept those surprises. I will let blessings come to me, rather than trying to grab what I think I need."

Giving voice to my commitment left me feeling relieved and excited, but also frightened. I knew this was a novel experiment, and that I would sometimes revert to my former self, the person who warded off anxiety by trying to control every aspect of her life.

To keep my commitment in mind, I typed up a new quote for the picture frame on my computer desk: *Let life happen through me.* I did not throw out the old words about swimming in the waters of my soul's purpose, the words I had so badly misinterpreted in the past. I left that beautiful quote in the picture frame, but covered it with the new quote, the one I need to look at now.

THE SPIRIT IS WILLING

In November 2013, Russ and I met with a contractor to talk about installing new siding on our house. We assumed he would begin the project when the weather warmed up in the spring.

"Oh, no," the contractor said. "My crew installs siding all year round." He placed us on his schedule for mid-December.

That winter ended up being the most brutal season I'd ever lived through. Michigan residents were repeatedly visited by polar vortexes that brought temperatures in the double-digits below zero. Along with the cold came vast amounts of snow.

The poor siding crew, wrapped from head to toe in their winter gear, arrived at our house in the middle of bitterly cold temperatures and a raging blizzard. I felt terribly sorry for the men, and certainly would have forgiven them if they had cancelled and rescheduled their appointment with us. But they persisted through the severe weather and completed their work.

Unfortunately, they were unable to do an adequate job of cleaning up their worksite, as the relentless snowfall immediately covered any nails or scraps of siding that fell to the ground.

Months later, when the snow finally melted, my husband and I discovered a yard filled with construction debris. It took us weeks to clean it up. Additionally, we found that the crew had trampled flowerbeds and damaged shrubbery all around our house.

The unusually harsh winter had also taken its toll on the plant life on our property. Hardy evergreen shrubs that had stood strong through countless winters now looked pitiful, as portions of their branches had died. The weight of the snow had broken deciduous shrubs, reducing them to piles of sticks. Between the weather and the construction job, our landscaping had been left in ruins.

However, during the month of May, our yard began showing signs of life again. A potted lavender plant had failed to survive the winter. But as I removed it from its container, I found an abundance of tiny lavender seedlings growing in the dirt around the pot. The plant had given new life at the time of its death. I gathered up the seedlings and planted them in a new location.

After I pruned the deadwood out of the deciduous shrubs, little was left of them. But that year, those shrubs grew thicker than they'd ever been. The damaged evergreen shrubs began showing new, bright green growth in the areas that had died.

The perennial herbs in one of my flowerbeds had been trampled by the heavy boots of the construction crew, and I was sure they would never grow again. But those intrepid plants sprung up lusher than ever before, spreading out onto the sidewalk and nearly blocking our passage around the house. Likewise, the irises, daylilies, Russian sage, and blazing stars grew unusually lush, their blooms offering a glorious display of color. Our yard was gorgeous that spring.

It seemed that, in some way, the harsh winter and the brutal trampling was good for those shrubs and flowers. The spiritual metaphor stunned me. I'd been feeling like I'd been trampled to the ground by my injury. But my plants told me that, even though parts of me had died, I had a myriad of opportunities to grow in new directions.

After leaving the Mennonite Church more than thirty years ago, I did a great deal of spiritual exploration. I sampled many different religions and traditions. Forsaking the somber rules of my upbringing, I chased down many enchanting and expansive spiritual experiences.

Sometimes, those experiences lured me down side streets that taught me little, except for what roads are best not taken.

Several times, I fell under the spell of con men, who tried to convince me they were the only ones who could show me the way. Such dishonorable fellows taught me a hard lesson, that whenever some self-proclaimed leader has me feeling confused, ungrounded, and self-doubting, it is time for me to get the heck away from him.

Many times, I thought I was headed toward something momentous, that light was shining on my path. I would become excited over serendipitous events, which I'd take as signs that the universe was smiling on me. But then my path would grow dark and rugged, and I'd find myself teetering on the edge of some rocky precipice.

Thankfully, I've had some wonderful teachers who have

broadened my spiritual perspectives. However, I have sometimes listened too intently to my teachers' voices, allowing them to drown out the voice of my own wisdom.

In 2007, I had my first encounter with ceremonial stones when I visited Stonehenge in England. Shortly after that, I had a dream in which I collected a pile of ceremonial stones of irregular shapes. Amazingly, when I laid them out, they fit together perfectly, like pieces in a jigsaw puzzle.

When I awoke, I immediately understood the meaning of the dream. I was, at that point in my life, in the process of collecting bits and pieces of spiritual truth from various sources, trying to fit them together into one cohesive whole. The picture had not yet clarified for me, but the dream told me that, someday, it would.

For a while after that dream, my spiritual seeking continued to be fragmented and disjointed. But in the years since my injury, I have seen the pieces of the puzzle come together. I find it much easier to hold my diverse spiritual experiences together in my heart and mind, without conflict or contradiction.

Surprisingly, this includes the religion of my childhood. In 2015 and 2017, I wrote a pair novels, *Blessed Transgression* and *Hope's New Season,* a family saga set in a Mennonite community. Telling the story of a struggling Mennonite family helped me work through painful feelings about my own upbringing.

Through this lengthy writing project, I ended up discovering new respect for the religious tradition into which I was born. Being raised in the Mennonite Church has taught me self-discipline, social consciousness, moral standards, and a strong work ethic. Additionally, I have fond feelings for the Mennonites' endearing cultural traditions and the support offered by the tightknit community.

However, when a traumatic brain injury shattered the life I'd known for so many years, no belief system I ever ascribed to was enough to provide the strength I needed just to get through my day. To find a spiritual source that could sustain me, I had to go deeper than I'd ever gone, to the level of unlabeled and uncategorized beliefs, to the comfort and wisdom that can only come from the divine spark within.

During the fifteen years prior to my injury, I had attempted to accelerate my spiritual progress by seeking the help of healers and teachers. I had looked to others for solutions to my life problems, and had believed that receiving a treatment or following a spiritual teaching could propel me down the path at a faster pace.

The weeks, days, and hours before my fateful accident, I had thought I was doing the right things, following the right prescription for success. But after my injury, I realized there are no magical formulas for negotiating spiritual growth.

Although I did receive several healing treatments following my injury, the sessions didn't mean as much to me as they had in the past. I knew that, ultimately, my growth would not come from what others did to me or for me. No treatment was going to rescue me from the task of coming to terms with my new reality, living with a brain injury.

I've come to understand that spiritual growth primarily results from the lessons we learn through negotiating difficult experiences. While we may enjoy moments of enchantment, the path also involves slogging through the hard times, making the best decisions possible, and discovering new inner resources when we think we've come to the end of our strength. After my brain injury, it seemed as if the spirit whispered to me, "If you really want to build spiritual capital, work your way through this challenge."

One day several years ago, as I was going about my household chores, a quiet thought came to me: *No matter what fate befalls me in this life, I will never lose faith.* In that random moment, I realized I had made an irreversible decision within my soul.

Knowing that my path will continue to be rugged at times, I have since made it a goal to become disappointment-proof. Essentially, I hope to arrive at a point where disappointment no longer throws me into a state of disillusionment, where I will never lose the resolve to pick myself up and start again.

When I was a young child, an elderly couple, Melvin and Millie, lived on a small farm a quarter of a mile down the road from us. One of my earliest childhood memories is peering out our living room window, watching flames engulf Melvin and Millie's house.

The house burned to the ground, and Melvin and Millie had no means to rebuild it. So, they picked themselves up and did the best they could with what resources they had left. They moved into a chicken coop on their property. Undaunted by the loss of her house, Millie turned that chicken coop into a charming little home. She kept it in immaculate condition.

I hope that, in the face of future losses, I will always follow Millie's example of resilience.

One challenge I struggle with now is the most intense loneliness I have ever felt in my life. As my husband works long hours and my ability to spend time in social settings has been compromised, I spend endless hours without companionship. But it has occurred to me that surviving this loneliness and learning the lessons my solitude teaches me will be a victory for me. I take comfort in my belief that the results of my efforts to cope with my injury may reap benefits that show up in future phases of my soul's journey.

I also believe that, in time, all things are fulfillment of divine will. Much of the time, I don't understand why certain things are happening to me. "Don't worry about the outcome," my inner wisdom whispers when I become worried and frantic. "Things will happen the way they should."

In 2014, when I was preparing to write *Blessed Transgression,* I felt confused and disheartened. I had a vague sense of what I wanted the story to convey, but my ideas were a jumbled mess. For some reason, they weren't streaming through my mind in the same way they had with previous novels.

Is my mind no longer receiving that kind of inspiration? I wondered. *Is my injured brain beginning to fail me? Are my writing days over?*

I decided to try an experiment. "I'm going to start this story," I announced to myself, "not knowing where it is going or how it will end. I will trust the process and have faith that the story will carry me wherever it needs to go. If this process doesn't work and I am unable to write this book, then I will accept that."

While knowing I was setting myself up for possible failure, I plunged into the writing. Amazingly, the story wrote itself. The way it emerged from my tangle of ideas was incomprehensible to me. The process was exhilarating.

This lesson in trust greatly reduced my fear of being blocked while writing subsequent books. I now know that even though the way may not reveal itself to me in the current moment, the ideas will inevitably come. When I grow tired and my thoughts became muddled, I know that resting will revive my brain and that fresh ideas will spring up later. Generally, the ideas have come quicker than I've expected them to. I have learned to maintain a receptive mind, trusting that inspiration will not fail me.

Obviously, this experience with my writing offers a lesson for trusting the flow of my entire life. Applying that lesson on a larger scale has been anything but easy. I've balked at giving up my habits of worrying and trying to control outcomes. Gradually, however, this lesson in trust is overtaking my consciousness.

Although I would prefer a path of spiritual bliss, I've learned that trauma, grief, and profound disappointment crack my heart open, allowing for more direct communication with the divine. In the early weeks after my injury, when it felt as if my brain had been battered beyond the point of recovery, I experienced a barrage of spiritual imagery and words, coming to me in dreams or spontaneously entering my thoughts. It seemed as if the cracks in my broken brain allowed light to come through. When things are going smoothly in my life, I experience less of this type of inspiration.

I've also learned that when the darkness of grief and disappointment consumes me, I can survive that agonizing journey until I arrive at a place of peace and understanding. Many a night since my injury, I've lain awake, tormented by old pain or overwhelmed by feelings of hopelessness in the face of current challenges.

My natural inclination is to do something to avoid the pain. But I am learning to embrace it, to stay with it, even at times when it feels as if I've been stripped of everything I have and reduced to nothing. If I keep slogging my way through the dark tunnel, I eventually come to a cool-headed, dispassionate view of my troubling situation. My pain begins to feel less horrific, less personal, and more like a part of the human condition. In that place, I find compassion for myself and all others who share my experience.

At such times, I have more of a sense of myself as a soul. I know that even if my ego is reduced to tatters, my soul is alive and well, robust and indestructible. Even at those times when I feel like half a person, I know that I have a full soul.

Sometimes, it seems impossible to hear the inner voice of wisdom within when my nerves are screaming in agony. I've come to understand that the dysfunction of my fragile brain does not reflect the condition of my spirit. I know that my body throws up many distractions that get in the way of spiritual clarity, but I am learning to see them for what they are. Emotional difficulties and cognitive meltdowns expose the weakness of my human condition, but they do not define who I am on a fundamental level.

As a lifelong perfectionist, I am constantly frustrated by the fact that the creativity I desire to express in this life cannot be supported by my limited human brain and body. I am beginning to accept that, despite my best efforts, I never will come close to manifesting perfection while inhabiting this body.

I have often longed to hear the voice of God telling me that I am loved despite my imperfection, that I deserve to be alive, and that I have a reason for being here.

One night in December 2012, I dreamt that I was traveling in the spirit world. I came upon a man who, while living on earth, had been executed for committing a violent crime. He was now existing in a state of abject darkness and alienation. He stood with his back to me, cut off from light and love. I had never encountered spiritual darkness of that nature.

As I gazed at the wretched man, I experienced a deep knowing that God's love extends to everyone, and that no one is outside that love. Not even someone who had done something as despicable as this man had done.

"Your soul is held by me in love," I said to the man.

He was unresponsive to my words, unyielding.

"Try to let the love in," I urged.

Then he turned to face me. He was smiling, and his countenance was beginning to glow with light. "I will," he said.

The dream seemed to have deep implications for me, but I couldn't grasp its full import. I recorded it in my journal. Then, a few months later, I discussed it with my priest, Father John. He suggested an interpretation that I hadn't considered before.

"The man in darkness," he said, "represents the parts of yourself that you've rejected, parts that feel despicable, unworthy, and unlovable. By extending God's love to the man, you were claiming it for yourself as well."

At first, it was difficult to accept Father John's thoughts about the dream. I didn't want to admit to identifying in any way with the man existing in such spiritual darkness. However, the more I think about it, the more I am comforted by my priest's explanation.

Despite periods of struggling through darkness, I am also reminded that the spiritual journey is meant to be a joyful one. I was raised to live a life of discipline, sacrifice, and self-denial. It has taken me a long time to understand that spirituality also involves enjoying and appreciating the life I've been given.

Two years after my injury, I had a dream in which I heard the following words: "When we walk with the Spirit, we move so lightly that it's like walking on air."

Four years later, I had a dream in which I was twirling and dancing in ecstasy. When I awoke, I was hit with a startling thought: *Joy is my right.* At that moment, the thought held such conviction that any dour outlook on life had no chance to stand up against it.

Admittedly, I have not yet reached a point of maintaining a consistently joyful attitude. In that regard, I have a lot of growth ahead of me. I tend to fall back into thoughts of not being good enough, not having accomplished enough, or not having enough love in my life. But when I catch myself ruminating on such thoughts, I remind myself that I am much better served by living in gratitude. When I succeed in shifting my thoughts toward what I am grateful for, I feel a change in my entire being.

When I watch the news on television, I am reminded of all the people on this planet who are victims of war, crime, natural disasters, and debilitating illness. Many others struggle with addictions that bankrupt their lives in every conceivable way. It seems unthinkable that I should ever feel sorry for myself, that I should be anything less than grateful.

Until recent years, I have tended to live with my focus set on the future. My inclination has been to work hard, discounting the present moment while preparing for a better time to come. I have often fallen into such thoughts as, *When I get this project done, then I can relax and enjoy my life.* Of course, when the task in question would be completed, another one would quickly take its place, and the long-awaited moment of enjoyment would be pushed farther ahead into the future.

I am beginning to realize that the moment I've always been waiting for is *now*. Each moment is a point in time in which I can fully experience the sweetness of life, in which I can live in joy and gratitude. In every moment, my life is complete.

Throughout much of my adult life, I have been told that I spend too much time in my head. "You should be more in your body," well-meaning advisors have intoned. Their criticism has never failed to annoy me, as living in my thoughts and imagination seems to be what comes naturally to me.

But I am also aware of the fact that dissociating from my body has been a way of seeking self-protection. Inhabiting a body has sometimes seemed dangerous to me. It has rendered me vulnerable to the pain associated with assault, both physical and emotional.

Since my injury has altered my sensory experience in the world, having my soul inhabit a body sometimes seems odd to me. The body itself seems weird. It requires food and sleep to sustain itself. It is forced to deal with waste products. It engages in a most peculiar reproductive process. It bleeds, it suffers debilitating pain. It is ruined by disease and injury. It inevitably declines with age.

Many times, I have wished to escape the challenges of a malfunctioning brain by soaring out of my body. Yet, I consider it an act of spiritual devotion to be willing to inhabit my less-than-perfect body, to learn the lessons that come with living in a compromised state.

I have made the commitment to do the best I can with my human form so long as I am meant to inhabit it. I exercise regularly, pay attention to my nutrition, and lead a healthy lifestyle. I attend to my medical needs. No doubt, I am prolonging my life through these conscientious actions. Something in me must want to stay alive.

Years ago, I had a psychotherapy client named Kenneth, a man who suffered from mild cognitive impairment. He was determined to live independently, but didn't quite possess the skills to manage life on his own. Consequently, he continually found himself in one jam after another. Some aspect of his life always seemed to be unraveling.

During the course of our therapeutic relationship, Kenneth was diagnosed with several serious health problems, conditions which he had difficulty managing. I tried to arrange help for him, which he declined. I often wondered how long he would live, and even how much investment he had in staying alive.

One beautiful spring day in the middle of all his trials, Kenneth came into my office and described to me what it felt like to have the gentle breeze blow against his face and ruffle his hair. "It makes it worth it to be alive," he said.

I marveled at this bit of profundity coming from a man who generally would not be viewed as a source of wisdom. His life was falling apart in every conceivable way. Still, he found reasons to be grateful for that life.

In the years since my injury, I have often recalled Kenneth's words. One summer day in 2017, I sat in my living room recliner, ruminating on thoughts about the pointlessness of existing in my brain-injured state. Then I felt the sunlight coming through the window, warming the skin on my bare arm, and I remembered that I am grateful to be alive.

December of that same year was a time of low energy for me, and I repeatedly lapsed into thinking of myself as someone in a state of half-existence. But while sitting in meditation one evening, I noticed that my breathing was strong and vital. Oddly, that took me by surprise. A thought hit me: *You are fully alive, and you still have life ahead of you.*

Despite my aggravation with those who criticize me for living in my head, I am forced to agree with them. I now recognize that when I fully inhabit my body instead of trying to escape it, I feel more connected with the divine source of my life. At the times when my nervous system is not overwhelmed, I try to focus on experiencing the pleasure of what I see, hear, taste, feel, and smell. Paradoxically, appreciating the world of the senses turns me toward the world of the spirit.

One day in August 2016, I sat with my priest in his office at the church, telling him about my spells of deep fatigue and my struggle with mental confusion. Father John was about to retire, not because he wanted to, but because health problems were rapidly rendering him incapable of providing service to the parish.

We shared our grief over having to prematurely surrender our careers. We talked about the further health challenges that might be in store for each of us, wondering how we would cope. Then Father John told me a story about a man he'd visited, whose illness had stripped him of almost every ability he had.

"I can't take this anymore," the man had said. "I don't have anything left."

"What you have left," Father John told him, "is your continuing conversation with God."

HEALING THE WORLD

Throughout my years of working as a therapist, I always hoped I was doing my part in healing the troubles of the world. After I was forced to relinquish my career, my heart stayed with my former work. Since my injury, I've had countless dreams about being a therapist, and I always awake from them feeling wistful.

But now, when I listen to people launch into accounts of their personal problems, I often feel overwhelmed. I recently encountered a stranger in a public place who began talking to me about her domestic troubles. I tried to be gracious, to listen, and to wish her well. But hearing her story overloaded me, throwing me into a cognitive shutdown. As I drove the familiar streets back to my home, I was so dazed that I had difficulty finding my way.

I can't stand up to this kind of thing anymore, I admitted to myself.

I often think about the times during my career when I talked with trauma and abuse victims all day long. Even though the work was highly stressful, I had the strength to do it. But I no longer possess that kind of stamina. Doing that type of work is no longer my role in life. It is now someone else's job.

What role do I play now in helping the planet? I've ask myself countless times. *Is there anything a person with a brain injury can offer?*

One night in February 2017, I went to bed feeling depressed and energetically drained. I awoke in the early hours of the morning feeling so terrible that I prayed for divine help.

After falling asleep again, I had a surreal dream. I was sitting alone in a room, when a strange little man in a wheelchair wheeled himself through the door to join me. He was clearly disabled, missing both legs and one arm, but he appeared to be happy and cheerful. He wheeled his chair behind me and began giving me a back massage with his one remaining hand. It felt wonderful.

When he was finished, he said, "Goodnight, Lois." Then he wheeled himself out of the room. The minute he left, I awoke from the dream, my back vibrating with rejuvenating energy. Truly, it felt as if I'd been touched by a divine hand. I thanked both God and my dream friend.

When I recounted the dream to my husband, he stated the obvious: "It means that you still have something important to contribute, even if you have a disability."

During the years prior to my injury, when I was deeply involved in spiritual exploration, I often encountered the prediction that our planet was about to enter an era of love and light. This was envisioned as a time when peace and justice would prevail on earth, when health and prosperity would be available to all.

Sometimes, dates were even projected as to when this enlightened era would dawn upon us. In December 2009, less than a year prior to my injury, I wrote a comical poem about such a time. It began with the following:

Good friends, we're approaching two thousand and ten.
Who would ever believe we'd survive until then?
A decade ago, we lived through an event.
The Y2K scare, it came and it went.
But now we are hearing another prediction
That many believe with utmost conviction.
Some people, they say our times are a-changing,
That our cosmic forces are all rearranging.
According to those endowed with insight,
Twenty ten ushers in the Era of Light.

Then I went on to describe amusing ways in which such an era would impact the delivery of mental health services. I shared the poem with my coworkers.

Humor aside, I have long hoped for the arrival of such an enlightened age. But as I write this chapter, our world appears to be far from the era of love and light. I weep as I watch news on TV about gun violence, terrorist activity, the unjust treatment of minority populations, and the threat of nuclear warfare. Racial and religious prejudice has reared its ugly head in ways that shock us all. Cruel, autocratic leaders maintain a tenacious hold on power in various parts of the world. Our current presidential administration is awash with scandal. Computer hackers violate our privacy and steal our personal information. Catastrophic weather events, which scientists believe are caused by global warming, pummel the planet mercilessly.

I am deeply saddened when I consider the possibility that I may not see the changes I want to see during my lifetime. "What can I possibly do to help?" I ask myself repeatedly.

I would love to be out in the streets protesting injustice and marching for good causes. I would love to make my voice heard in townhall meetings. But I know full well what would happen if I attempted to engage in such activities. I would break down very quickly from the level of noise and commotion. I would become cognitively disoriented and emotionally overwrought, and my gait would deteriorate. Someone would need to be there to take care of me. And it would take the better part of a week for me to recover from such an event.

I am deeply grateful for those who are able to take a more active role in advocating for victims of abuse and injustice in our country and around the world. These noble people have my blessing, and I pray for them. I sign numerous petitions and occasionally donate money for victims of natural disasters. I try to do my part in protecting the environment. I exercise my right to vote. Thankfully, the absentee ballot spares me from dealing with the commotion in the public polling place.

One day after watching depressing news on television, I got up to do some chores in my kitchen. An odd thought came to me: *One antidote to hearing such overwhelming negativity is to do my daily tasks cheerfully.*

Despite all the darkness in the world around us, I hang on to the belief that if we each cultivate our own spiritual light, our collective light will someday shine bright enough to overpower the darkness. I believe our collective light will shape our government's policies. I believe it will impact how neighbors deal with neighbors, and how nations deal with nations.

Perhaps if we say even one kind word or hold one hand, we are helping the entire planet. If we can do nothing else, living peacefully with those around us contributes to the light. Living with an attitude of joy and gratitude is the least we can do.

In August 2017, the death of a counter-protester during the white supremacist march in Charlottesville, Virginia, rocked the nation and sent shockwaves of pain through me.

Two days after that horrific event, I had a dental appointment. My dentist is from South Korea, and his assistant that day was Hispanic. And there was me, with my European Mennonite/Amish heritage. As the two of them bent over me in their work, it suddenly struck me that we represented three different ethnicities clustered tightly together, focused on a common goal, relating to each other in perfect peace. It felt wonderful to be living in a moment of racial and cultural harmony.

One morning in April 2017, I woke up despondent, feeling incompetent and worthless. In an attempt to combat those dark emotions, I began working on the task of repotting an aloe plant, preparing to take it outdoors for the warm weather season. When I stepped back to look at my handiwork, I was stunned by how beautiful the aloe looked in its new pot.

As I visualized adding a trailing red vine to the pot to add color contrast, I realized how much joy such work brought me. *Surely,* I mused, *if I complete my work with joy and serenity, no matter how insignificant it might seem, it must do something to bring healing to the world.*

Several days later, I was outside working in my flower gardens. A woman who lived in a nearby apartment came over to talk with me. We had never met before.

"I see you working out here all the time," she said. "You have such good ideas." Then she informed me that she was getting ready to move to a place out in the country, and that my gardening had given her inspiration for the planting she wanted to do at her new home.

I was shocked. Gardening feels like my last grasp on competence, one last way I can be creative. Gardening gives me something to do when I am cut off from so many other activities. It is something I hang onto with desperation, as losing my ability to garden would mean losing another big part of myself. It was hard for me to believe that, in engaging in this therapeutic activity, I was inspiring someone else.

Is this now my way of helping to heal the world? I wondered. *I'm not out in the public counseling trauma victims, rescuing people from natural disasters, or lobbying to change social policies. But perhaps creating beauty in my yard is still helping others. And it is something I can do with utmost joy.*

Maybe, I went on to think, *every time I water a plant or feed an animal, I am helping the world.*

My thoughts turned to a psychotherapy client I'd seen years earlier. David had been at a low point in his life. He was unemployed, penniless, going through a divorce, and sleeping on a relative's couch. Furthermore, this otherwise able-bodied young man was suffering from a pinched nerve in his neck that caused him unbearable pain. Formerly a hard worker in a factory, he was now unable to lift anything.

David had a friend who kept horses on his farm. He had, in the past, enjoyed helping his friend take care of the horses. Now unable to lift a bale of hay, David described to me how he would hold out a handful of hay for a horse to munch on.

"I just want to be a part of things," he told me. I knew what he was referring to: the circle of giving, nurturing, and healing in which we are all involved.

As the 2017 Christmas season approached, marked by lavish decorations in stores, television ads for must-have products, and news reports about how much money consumers were expected to spend on gifts, I felt the energy drain from my system. I had no heart for participating in the mad rush that year. Contracting a nasty cold virus further weakened me, adding to my holiday depression.

But in the midst of the weakness and darkness, an idea came to me. For years, I had been a halfhearted participant in our national holiday traditions. Celebrating holidays had become an obligation, rather than a joy. I suddenly knew it was time to unburden myself of those worn-out practices, and to do something that came from my heart.

I knew I wanted to celebrate holidays in a way that transcended all cultural, religious, and racial divides. I wanted to celebrate something that reflected the common experience of all inhabitants of the earth. Something not tainted by commercialism. Something that showed my respect for the planet that sustains our lives.

I ran my idea past my husband and children, and was pleasantly surprised when they expressed enthusiasm for my new plan. So, we have decided to create our own family holidays. We have committed ourselves to celebrating the changing of each season: winter solstice, spring equinox, summer solstice, and autumn equinox.

The changing seasons are something everyone experiences, albeit in different ways, no matter what our race, religion, or country of origin. Each season is rife with metaphors, offering wisdom for the phases of our own lives. My family now celebrates each of our seasonal holidays with simple décor, music, readings, and food pertinent to that season. At each holiday, we make a donation to some organization that directly benefits the wellbeing of the planet and its inhabitants.

I've come to realize that one refuge I have in the midst of the turmoil on the planet is to live more in tune with the earth. While my injury has cut me off from many societal activities, living close to the earth helps me feel more at home here. I hope that celebrating holidays in a more heartfelt way will lead me to take other steps toward living a more heartfelt life.

When I was attending my medical exercise program, I met a man named Jack. He was obviously disabled, with a severe curvature of the spine that appeared to make standing and walking difficult for him. Yet, he came to the gym on a regular basis, working diligently to strengthen himself.

On November 9, 2016, the day after our national election, the entire country was abuzz about the newly elected president. Many, including myself, were disbelieving and disheartened.

At the gym that day, I fumed and muttered to friends about the outcome of the election. Then I came upon Jack in the middle of his workout. He was wearing a tee shirt emblazoned with a peculiar slogan: "It takes all types."

"What does that saying on your shirt mean?" I asked him.

He looked up at me and smiled. "I got this shirt from giving blood," he said.

I chuckled. "Oh, I see. All types. That's clever."

"I've donated over thirty gallons of blood in my lifetime," he informed me. "It's my way of giving back."

"Wow," I said. "That's impressive. What type of blood do you have?"

"A positive," he replied. "I wish I had type O blood. That would make me a universal donor, and I could help more people."

Suddenly, I saw Jack in a new light. He was clearly a strong man, not someone to be pitied for his disability. I walked away from that conversation grateful for the "feel good" story in the middle of unsettling national news.

But Jack's words also sparked in me the idea of becoming a donor myself. I had donated blood several times as a young adult, but it had been decades since I'd even considered doing that again. I had been too busy with school and career. I knew I met all the medical criteria to become a donor. Now, it seemed selfish to withhold my help from those who needed it.

Eight months later, when I received an email notice that an organization called *Michigan Blood* was holding a drive at our local hospital, I signed up to be a donor. I have since donated blood every couple of months, and will continue to do so for as long as I can.

As Jack said, I consider this a way of giving back. Not by offering my words or actions, but by sharing something of my own life essence. The act of donating blood feels very personal, very satisfying. I feel most fortunate to be able to do this.

Since I now know something about the pain of living with a disability, it behooves me to be considerate of those who struggle with conditions more debilitating than mine.

One day as I was walking toward the door of the medical center in which my exercise program was held, a car pulled up to the curb. Under the solicitous care of his companion, a disabled man got out. It appeared that he had suffered paralysis on one side of his body from a stroke. Judging by the relative youthfulness of his face, I suspected that he had become disabled much earlier in life than he'd ever expected.

Using a cane, he began traversing the short distance to the center's door, inching along at a snail's pace. I was walking rapidly, and had plenty of time to cross in front of him and move on into the building.

But I didn't. I recalled the countless times in the early months after my injury when I'd walked into public buildings with a halting, weird-looking gait. I remembered how humiliating that had been, how it felt as if the entire world was watching my embarrassing performance.

Furthermore, I knew that even though I was now able to walk normally into public buildings, my gait frequently slowed to a crawl inside the building, due to the stimulation of light, noise, and commotion. I knew what it was like to have people rush around me or cut in front of me, as if I were an obstacle in their way.

I suspected this man had experienced countless times of being humiliated by other people's responses to his condition. I wanted to spare him another blow to his dignity. So, I stopped and waited while he inched his way toward the door.

I hope I never fail to open a door, offer a seat, or pick up a dropped object for someone less able than I am.

Recently, I had one of my recurring dreams about being a therapist. I was working with two young children whose criminal father was trying to gain custody of them. I felt protective of the children, and tried to block such an unfortunate event from happening. But I was unable to do so, and the father succeeded in obtaining custody. The children wanted to continue with therapy, but their father would not allow it. Sadly, I had to let go of my relationships with the children.

I was worried about these vulnerable little ones in the care of their despicable father, and was concerned about his influence on them. Yet, I had a counterthought. "These children will save their father," I commented to someone else in the dream. I knew that therapy had planted seeds in their minds that would sprout and grow, having later effects in their lives and impacting the life of their father.

When I awoke from the dream, a comforting, yet powerful, thought sprang into my mind: *The work I've done in the past is still alive in the present.*

I suddenly understood that whatever good I've ever managed

to do for anyone else still lives on, taking new shape in their lives, the effects rippling out to others. In the same vein, others have planted seeds that grew in me, influencing the life that I've lived and the work that I've done. I simply carried and nurtured something that someone else had started. And someone after me continues to carry that work forward.

We are not the originators of any of the work we do. Someone who came long before us started it. We pick it up, carry it for a while, and then pass it on to the next person. Thus, whatever good we do in healing the pain of the world is not an individual venture. The "work" is bigger than any of us. It just passes through our hearts and hands while we are here.

AUTHOR'S NOTE

This book started out as a shoebox full of random thoughts scribbled on scraps of paper. Organizing the ideas and shaping them into a book was almost more than my injured brain could manage. I apologize for any errors my struggling eyes failed to detect.

Both cognitively and emotionally, this was undoubtedly the most grueling writing project I have ever taken on. I am relieved that it's finally completed. But writing this book enabled me to delve into my deepest feelings about my injury, allowing for more healing. It has helped me come to a place of greater peace about what has happened to me. It has reinforced my coping skills and enabled me to find new, creative ways of living with a brain injury.

To the reader who has accompanied me on this journey, I thank you. If any condition stands in the way of your living a full life, may you find wholeness.

NOTE FROM AUTHOR'S HUSBAND

by A. R. Thomas

Prior to her brain injury, Lois was an independent woman, both professionally and personally. She was always working and learning in her profession as a clinical social worker. I know from encounters with her co-workers, her supervisors, and even some past clients that she was respected and admired for her caring attitude as well as her work ethic and professionalism. I also viewed her that way.

While at home, Lois always seemed to be busy with her hobbies and with making our home as pleasant an environment as possible. She took care of her indoor plants and outdoor gardens, made sure we kept the house clean, and still found time to paint or sculpt. She never seemed to tire of doing, learning, or expressing herself creatively. She took classes in Healing Touch. She studied Vedantic scriptures at the ashram. She took continuing education seminars to keep her social work license current.

Because of all this, I used to think she didn't really need me or anyone, and I felt like a burden to her. However, that all changed when she was struck by a car and sustained a traumatic brain injury. I witnessed the dramatic change in her personality from the confident professional caregiver to the patient needing care. I know that the most traumatic part of her injury was the juxtaposition of her new reality against her old reality. It was unbearable for her to experience, and painful for me to watch.

Lois has made great strides in dealing with the results of her brain injury. Not just the changes in vision and stamina, but also the emotional and spiritual challenges that come with any traumatic event in a person's life.

Finally, I want to share this with Lois's readers: remember that no matter how difficult it is to be with a loved-one who has suffered an event like this, it is always more painful and difficult for them than you can ever know. Love them more and help them when they need your help. Encourage them, but don't tell them things will get better, because some things may get worse.

So be there for them in body, mind, and spirit, and you may find, as I have, a change in yourself. Through the experience of living with a brain-injured wife, I have become a better partner and a better person in general. I am surprised by the change in me, and somewhat ashamed that it took my wife's suffering to make me a better person.

OTHER BOOKS BY LOIS JEAN THOMAS

www.loisjeanthomas.com

Me and You—We Are Who? (The Sambodh Society, Inc., 2006)

All the Happiness There Is (The Sambodh Society, Inc., 2006)

Johnny and Kris (The Sambodh Society, Inc., 2013)

Daughters of Seferina (Seventh Child Publishing/CreateSpace, 2013)

Days of Daze: My Journey Through the World of Traumatic Brain Injury (Seventh Child Publishing/CreateSpace, 2014)

Rachel's Song (Seventh Child Publishing/CreateSpace, 2014)

A.K.A. Suzette (Seventh Child Publishing/CreateSpace, 2014)

Blessed Transgression (Seventh Child Publishing/CreateSpace, 2015)

A Weekend with Frances (Seventh Child Publishing/CreateSpace, 2016)

Hope's New Season (Seventh Child Publishing/CreateSpace, 2017)

91271666R00130

Made in the USA
Columbia, SC
15 March 2018